THE CONTROL AND ASSURANCE OF QUALITY

by
C. L. (CHUCK) CARTER, JR.
Quality Assurance Consultant
President of
C. L. Carter, Jr. & Associates, Inc.
Management & Personnel Consultants
Dallas, Texas

Library of Congress Catalog Card Number: 68-59084

Taylor Publishing Company
Dallas, Texas

THE CONTROL AND ASSURANCE OF QUALITY

THIS BOOK IS DEDICATED TO THE
QUALITY, VALUE, SAFETY, SERVICE AND INTEGRITY OF
PEOPLE, PRODUCTS, AND PERSONAL SERVICES

I deeply appreciate all of the wonderful people who have helped me and worked with me over the years. My family, friends, business and professional associates, clients, and the good Lord above have made it all possible. I will always be grateful and hereby express a very humble 'thank you,' with special acknowledgements to: R. L. Cutright; W. D. Walker; G. M. Carter; I. M. Carter; C. L. Carter; W. Frazee; R. Kraus; S. J. Carter and C. L. Carter III.

C. L. (Chuck) Carter, Jr.

THE CONTROL AND ASSURANCE OF QUALITY

ABOUT THE AUTHOR

C. L. (Chuck) Carter, Jr., professional quality assurance consultant and president of C. L. Carter, Jr. and Associates, Inc., management and personnel consultants, Dallas, Texas, has over 18 years of industrial and business experience in all phases of quality management, engineering, and personnel in small, medium, and large companies engaged in commercial, industrial, and governmental markets. He is a graduate of Newark College of Engineering, a Senior Member of the American Society for Quality Control, and a Certified Quality Engineer. He is a national lecturer, teacher, author, and publisher of five books and a training and motivation film. Mr. Carter is a very active member of ASQC and is a member of the National ASQC Board of Directors, maintaining active membership in all Divisions and the Vendor-Vendee Technical Committee. He presents many technical and management papers each year and has been an active lecturer for the American Management Association for several years. He is very active in local ànd national training, management, engineering, and other professional societies; a member of the European Organization for Quality Control and a Senior Member of the American Society of Tool and Manufacturing Engineers. Chuck Carter is on the Board of Directors of companies and provides guidance, direction, and technical assistance to management and personnel.

"THE CONTROL AND ASSURANCE OF QUALITY"
TABLE OF CONTENTS

THE CONTROL AND ASSURANCE OF QUALITY

INTRODUCTION AND APPLICATION

Quality Assurance theory, application, and techniques apply to everyone in every walk of life as associated with Commercial, Industrial, Military, Space, Marine, Oceanography, Medical, Scientific, Educational, Business Offices, or Governmental organizations. Everyone is involved, including small, medium, and large business and industry. Everyone connected with manufacturing, chemical, oil, aerospace, electronics, communications, automotive, insurance, banking, hospitals, education, or personal services is involved with quality, value, and integrity. Yes, everyone is involved with the control and assurance of quality. Everyone is involved from the Sweeper to the Chairman of the Board; from the Student to the College Professor to the Dean. But, not everyone is interested! Very few people understand just how involved they are with quality, value, and integrity, the control and assurance of quality, and what their involvement means on a personal basis and in business relationships on a day-to-day basis.

Let's look at it this way ... If you do not possess quality, value, and integrity—if you do not have a personal plan for progress, growth, development, and success—if you do not care—if you do not have pride in yourself and in your work—if you do not try to do your very best in whatever you do—your personal or business competitor **WILL!** He, she, or they will be able to achieve control and assure success through quality, value, and integrity. We all have the need as individuals; as business people, in government, as a nation, and as a free world. We all should have quality, value, and integrity. We all must control and assure the quality of whatever we do.

Quality Assurance is a management concept and tool for achieving quality, reliability, value, reduced costs, safety, service, and integrity of personnel, products, and personal services.

THE CONTROL AND ASSURANCE OF QUALITY

Total Quality Assurance involves management and personnel working as a closely coordinated team of qualified individuals who communicate, coordinate, and cooperate to achieve success. You are a vital part of the total quality team.

Q — Quantity
U — Unification
A — Ability
L — Loyalty
I — Integrity
T — Teamwork
Y — You

V — Valuable
A — Acceptable
L — Labor
U — Universal
E — Everyone

I — Interest
N — Natural
T — Technique
E — Education
G — Growth
R — Reliable
I — Inspect
T — Test
Y — You

Without you, there would be no team. Without you, there would be no business, industry, or government.

Yes, you could be the broken link, the missing person, the uninformed person with the "I don't care" attitude. You could be the one who causes the problems. You could be the one who solves the problems! You could be a doctor, lawyer, student, teacher, engineer, nurse, businessman, salesman, insuranceman, banker, technician, machine operator, inspector, secretary, president, or chairman of the board. You could be most anyone.

But, who are you? What are you? Where are you? How did you get there? What are you doing there? Where are you going? How are you going to get there? Have you got what it takes? Do you have a Personal Plan for Progress? Do you have quality, value, and integrity? Does your organization have quality, value, and integrity? Stop and answer those questions. Now lay out your short and long-range plans. Follow your plans. Yes, planning is your most important personal project. But very few people or companies lay out a plan or program and then follow the plan, program, or system.

Just what is quality, value, and integrity? Just what does quality, value, and integrity mean . . . to you ?. . . to your organization? What's going on around you today in business, industry, government, and personal life? How involved are you in business, industry, government, and professional organizations? Do you want to be a professional person with pride, quality, value, workmanship, and professional integrity? Yes, you can. As individuals, we must be educated, trained, and motivated.

THE CONTROL AND ASSURANCE OF QUALITY

Small business, large corporations, and government organizations must be motivated, educated, and trained. Educate, train, and motivate yourself, your business, your management, and your customers in all aspects of The Control and Assurance of Quality.

It is the intent of this book to provide guidance, direction, technical assistance, and to help you to understand and apply the theory, application, and techniques of total quality assurance, which is based on quality, value, and integrity of people, products, and personal services. This document is for: board chairman; presidents; vice presidents, and all other executives and managers; engineers; manufacturing personnel; purchasing personnel; quality, reliability, value and maintainability personnel; marketing, sales, and contract administration personnel; business people; government people; doctors, nurses, and hospital personnel; lawyers; bankers and accountants; students, educators, teachers, and counselors; industrial relations and personnel people; automobile personnel; insurance people; advertising, public relations, newspaper, radio, television and associated personnel; and for everyone of you, whatever your job may be. THIS BOOK IS FOR YOU ...

THE CONTROL AND ASSURANCE OF QUALITY

THINK WELL OF YOUR COMPANY

Wherever you're working, in office or shop,
And however far you may be from the top—
And though you may think you're just treading the mill,
Don't ever belittle the job that you fill.

For however little your job may appear—
You're just as important as some little gear,
That meshes with others in some big machine,
That helps keep it going, though never is seen.

They could do without you, we'll have to admit,
But business keeps on, when the big fellows quit,
And always remember, my lad, if you can,
The job's more important (oh, yes) than the man.

So if you hope to stay off the shelf,
Think more of your job, than you do of yourself.
Your job is important, don't think it is not,
So try hard to give it the best that you've got.

And don't ever think you're of little account—
Remember, you're part of the total amount.
If they didn't need you, you wouldn't be there,
So always, my lad, keep your chin in the air.

A digger of ditches, mechanic, or clerk—
Think well of your company, yourself, and your work.

—Unknown

THE CONTROL AND ASSURANCE OF QUALITY

WORDS OF WISDOM TO REMEMBER

It's a funny thing about life: If you refuse to accept anything but the best, you very often get it.

W. Somerset Maugham

The school of experience never gives its graduates a sheep-skin, but it does provide them with a tough hide.

George E. Mayo

You can't sit on the lid of progress. If you do, you will be blown to pieces.

Henry Kaiser

The quality of excellence can be developed in any field and is needed in all.

Lloyd W. Ashby

The attainment of a goal requires a definite plan of action even though this plan may change.

Lawrence A. Appley

Quality is made up of good workmanship, good material and good design.

Royal Bank of Canada Letter

'Qualified People' are your most important asset. 'People' are one of your major problems.

Chuck Carter

Idea power is the most tremendous human force in the world.

Herman W. Seinwerth

Progress is the sum of small victories won by individual human beings.

Bruce Catton

Willingness to seek and accept advice is one of the characteristics of successful men.

Dean Johnson

Time is an asset which we cannot lightly afford to waste.

George Bernard Shaw

The price of greatness is responsibility.

Sir Winston Churchhill

Time is the most valuable thing a man can spend.

Theophrastus

Every employee ought to be well informed. We ought to be able to state clearly what we expect.

John Mulhearn

THE CONTROL AND ASSURANCE OF QUALITY

WORDS OF WISDOM TO REMEMBER

Be concerned with today's opportunities, not yesterday's achievements.
Wilbur M. McFeely

Men, in teaching others, learn themselves.
Seneca

Planning is your most important personal project.
Chuck Carter

Every great work ever accomplished by man was called impossible ... at first.
Unknown

If the job is too easy, anybody can do it.
Unknown

Good books are a short cut to experience.
Clifton Fadiman

It's a mark of greatness when a person can receive and profit by constructive criticism from another.
Unknown

The path of least resistance is failure.
Unknown

The most important aspect of decision making is distinguishing between the significant and the trivial.
Unknown

Professional talent is truly the key to a successful team, whether it be a baseball, football or management team.
Chuck Carter

Advice is seldom welcome. Those who need it most, like it least.
Unknown

Some men rise to the occasion, while others merely go up in the air.
Unknown

If you have always done it that way, it probably is wrong.
Anon.

Before flaring up at the faults of others, pause and count ten ... of your own.
Unknown

Quality and Safety are always in season.
Unknown

THE CONTROL AND ASSURANCE OF QUALITY

WORDS OF WISDOM TO REMEMBER

The Leader does not say "Get Going"! Instead he says, "Let's Go".

Unknown

Let's put some TNT into our efforts ... A little more of the "TODAY ... NOT TOMORROW" philosophy.

Unknown

Indecision is frequently worse than taking a chance on the wrong decision.

Unknown

Giving it another try is better than an alibi.

Unknown

Intelligence, like muscle, must be exercised if it is to be ready for use when needed.

William B. Terhune

It isn't your position but your disposition that makes you happy or unhappy.

Unknown

The ladder to the top is one nobody holds for you.

Unknown

It takes 13 facial muscles to smile and 47 to frown.

Unknown

Don't do effectively that which shouldn't be done at all.

Unknown

We can make of life a stumbling block or a stepping stone.

Unknown

The reputation for quality is not easily earned. It is based on the skill of craftsmen, the use of high quality materials, and uncompromising attention to workmanship and details.

Anon.

The problem doesn't know the name of the company.

Chuck Carter

Everyone is responsible for the control and assurance of Quality. Our goal must be to 'Qualify the Unqualified'.

Chuck Carter

Chapter 1

QUALITY ASSURANCE HISTORY

In the beginning, we had "Craftsmen" who knew their trade, their product, and their customers. They were taught by their fathers, grandfathers, journeymen, and other craftsmen. These people, in every phase of Business, Industry, Educational and Governmental organizations had deep and dedicated pride in their work, their business, their product, and their satisfied customers. They took great pains to be exacting on the tolerances, the form, fit, function, and master-craftsmenlike quality of workmanship. They designed and made Quality Products of outstanding workmanship and true value in every respect. The Integrity of Product, Personnel and Service was inscribed by the name of the maker, the company, and their combined word of honor. Superior Quality and Craftsmanship was built-in. A man didn't release the item until it was Superior, Acceptable to him, and Worthy of bearing his name. Quality Assurance was a Personal Product of a man's Integrity. Quality Assurance was his Pride of Workmanship. Quality, Value and Integrity was his way of life.

In the beginning, we had small, one man companies. Slowly, we grew larger and larger in all Businesses, Industries and Government. This growth created problems.

The independent "Craftsman", who created, designed, fabricated and completed his product, became the victim of "Volume and Production." The Mass Production, or Specialization Age, took over, and the "true craftsman" began to fade away. It became commonplace for a person to do "one operation", and never have the opportunity to see the finished product. It also became common for the individual to lose interest, become bored, and not care about the finished item, or total management system of operation. That is, if management had a planned quality program or system!! In most cases, management caused the individual to lose interest. The individual became a number, and, as such, did what he had to do and no more. Management created and designed many, many of the "People Problems" we have today. Management must now try to re-design. Management must now try to re-establish the craftsmen, and re-develop the pride of the person in the work they are doing. Management's task will be long, hard, and in many cases, unrewarding. I say "unrewarding" because management is trying to rebuild craftsmanship back into the person. This task is unlimited in scope, because it encompasses **everyone** from the sweeper to the chief executive officer of the firm. This task can be likened to women's fashions or automobile options. In either case, we seem to reach a "point of extreme", and then we must go back to where we have been—to start all over again. For example: The fashions of the "roaring 20's" are being created as new and exciting innovations for the teenaged set. The "Flapper of 1927" is known as "Twiggy of 1967". The Standard Transmission or stick shift of 1937 is now the "3 or 4 in the floor" of 1967 and 1968. It wouldn't surprise me to see running boards and window shades as optional extras! These were original equipment in 1932! Look forward to the return of the rumble seat as the "very latest" for the younger (and older) generation of sport car owners.

Many years ago, the craftsman was his own best inspector. The Quality was created, designed, and built-in by the craftsman. Many years ago, mass production created the need for independent Inspection Organizations to impartially appraise the work of the Mass Production media. Separate Inspection Organizations were established, and, in time, these grew into large, powerful functions within major companies. Some of these Inspection Organizations became so powerful, they were literally dictating and governing the production operations. Instead of speeding up production, they were actually slowing down, or bogging down, the Production Efforts. This was done by Ridiculous Paper work functions and by having one Inspector for every one or two production operators. This type of inspection, as inflicted by non-management managers, was inefficient and very expensive. This was a major contributing cause of conflict between Production, Inspection, and Executive levels of Management. This led to Inspection being known as the "Necessary Evil" function of the organization. This terminology is still used today throughout industry. It will take years of Education, Training, Motivation and Professional Guidance, Direction, Technical Assistance and Corrective Action by all levels of Quality Management and Personnel, to erase the "Necessary Evil" terminology and philosophy.

The Inspection Organization gradually progressed from the primary appraisal function into more scientific areas of Quality Control through Statistical Sampling Plans, Control Charts, and an organized approach to Prevention rather than "After the Fact" detection. Scientific control, scientific studies, effective sampling techniques, and professional quality management planning for long term progress and growth, by such organizations as the Western Electric Company and the Bell Telephone Laboratories were the pioneering originators of the true

Quality Assurance concepts and philosophies we are all trying to achieve today.

Western Electric is now achieving their Quality Assurance Plan, which is based on the Sound Philosophy of Quality Assurance as a major contributor to cost reduction and/or elimination of Inspection through explicit Workmanship Standards, Process Controls, and Qualified Personnel accepting their true responsibility for the quality of their work. They are gradually removing the Inspection function, while increasing the reliability and life of the product with Acceptable Quality Levels being maintained within established attainable standards.

A lesson can be learned from historical evidence of Establishing a Quality Assurance Management Plan, and Working to the Plan to achieve realistic, attainable Management Goals. This has been successfully accomplished. We shall explore the ways and means of attaining Quality Assurance at the lowest cost for everyone concerned, in all areas of business, industry, education, government, and personal services.

Remember, the reputation for quality is not easily earned. It is based on the skill of craftsman, the use of highest quality materials, and uncompromising attention to workmanship and details.

Chapter 2

UNDERSTANDING THE DEFINITIONS

Understanding the terms, words, phrases and definitions becomes a major task in establishing an understanding of Quality Assurance and associated professional areas.

In reviewing the following definitions, you will find conflicts from company to company, and organization to organization. This is compounded by the fact that all companies and individuals are, and want to be, different. To illustrate this fact, I can relate some of the new titles and job classifications being generated by companies today. "Manager of Product Integrity" is also known as a Quality Control Manager or Director of Quality Assurance; "Produceability Manager or Engineer" is also known as Industrial Engineering Manager, Director of Manufacturing Engineering, or Methods Engineering Manager; "Procurement Manager" and "Materials Manager" is also known as Purchasing Manager, Director of Purchasing, or Purchasing Agent. These are but a few. There are many, many more. It appears that everyone is Title Conscious, and trying to develop a new unknown department for management and personnel to cope with. Management says it 'Sounds Impressive', and the Personnel Recruiting Representative says 'What is it?' I usually pass by saying, 'What else is new?' Keeping up with the Joneses next door is giving way to company confusion, competition in marketing, and new communication barriers.

I would like for you to be familiar with, and have a basic understanding of, the following terms and definitions.

1. **Quality Assurance:**
   "A Management discipline consisting of a planned and systematic program covering ALL functions and actions necessary to provide adequate confidence that the end item or service will perform satisfactorily in actual operation, thereby assuring customer satisfaction. A Management Program which includes Quality Control, Calibration, Reliability, Value Analysis, Training, Zero Defects and Integrity."
2. **Quality Control:**
   "A Management function to control the quality of articles to conform to quality standards."
3. **Calibration:**
   "Comparison of a measurement standard or instrument of known accuracy with another standard or instrument to detect, correlate, re-

port, or eliminate by adjustment, any variation in the accuracy of the item being compared.

4. **Reliability:**
   "The probability that a system or part will perform a required function under specified conditions without failure, for a specified period of time."
5. **Value Analysis:**
   "An organized effort directed at analyzing the function of any system, equipment, facilities and supplies for the purpose of achieving the required function at the lowest over-all cost, consistent with requirements for performance, quality, reliability, maintainability, delivery, and service."
6. **Training:**
   "A continuous program of learning to gain knowledge and improve one's ability in any subject, art or profession. Developing skills and attitudes through self-teaching, working on-the-job, workshop seminars, or formal classroom instruction."
7. **Zero Defects: Do it Right the First Time: Total Impact Program**
   "An organized effort to motivate and inspire personnel at all levels in an organization to do their jobs right the first time, every time. The elimination of defects attributable to human error. A dedicated approach for preventing defects by identifying and removing the cause. An appeal to the individual's pride of workmanship, self interest, loyalty and integrity."
8. **Integrity:**
   "The completeness of an entirely integrated and honest management concept of operation which includes the Policies, Plans, Personnel, Procedures, the Product and/or Service."

I realize the definitions of the stated professional terms can be interpreted to fit particular conditions and circumstances. These definitions are presented to establish a unification of management thoughts, concepts, interpretation and use. We must all try to speak and understand the same language. Additional definitions are covered throughout this book and in our other publications. We must all try to communicate, coordinate, and cooperate to achieve our management and personnel goals.

The following "Ten Points of Quality" may provide you with a clearer understanding of the term 'Quality'.

1. **QUALITY IS THE "EXTRA SOMETHING"**, the distinction that causes a product to stand out in its field.
2. **QUALITY REFLECTS ITS MAKER.** Pride of workmanship, experience, care shown in every product.
3. **QUALITY IS A BRAND NAME.** Products are bought when customers recognize and trust a familiar trade mark or company.
4. **QUALITY IS A BUILDER.** Century-old companies gained and held success by providing good products and good service for its customers.
5. **QUALITY IS AN ATTITUDE.** The personal attitudes of employees toward their job, their company, their products will determine the degree of product quality.
6. **QUALITY IS MANY PEOPLE.** Every person is responsible for quality.
7. **QUALITY IS PLANNED.** As a company, we must plan to make a top-quality product at a reasonable price and deliver on schedule.
8. **QUALITY, RELIABILITY AND VALUE** of our products are always remembered by the customer long after the cost is forgotten.
9. **QUALITY, PRICE AND DELIVERY** (or P. D. Q.) are achieved when the job is done "Right the First Time."
10. **TOTAL QUALITY ASSURANCE IS THE TEAMWORK APPROACH TO SATISFIED CUSTOMERS.**

I would suggest that you refer to the Definitions and Ten Points of Quality from time to time in an effort to motivate and stimulate your thinking with reference to Quality, Value and Integrity for the control and assurance of quality.

Chapter 3

TRAINING AND MOTIVATION

A Total Impact Program

Management direction and support is the most decisive and important factor in establishing a well planned motivation program. The first and most important element of the plan is the formulation of objectives.

The basic management objectives should be quality, value, and integrity of their company and its policies, programs, procedures, personnel, and products.

I firmly believe in training, motivation, and qualification of management and personnel at all levels of every organization. We present and conduct seminars and courses for individuals and client companies on the control and assurance of quality. A partial list of colleges and organizations who conduct seminars and courses is included at the end of this chapter. I have also provided a reference list of known books on 'Quality and Reliability' and an extensive list on 'Statistics'. The list is by Author—Title and Publisher. Please use it to your best advantage.

Training and motivation should be achieved by a well planned, maintained and continuing program, under the guidance and direction of the quality assurance organization in concert with the personnel department as an integral part of the total quality assurance program throughout the company. There should be no exceptions. Quality, value, cost reduction, safety, service, profit, and integrity must be the prime motivating forces. The program should be based on understanding by all levels of management and personnel, and should be installed quietly, efficiently, and effectively. This is like a sales program with a theme of "think quality and produce quality".

I do not advocate the use of the Army, Navy, Air Force, Governors, or other government dignitaries as being necessary to 'blast off' a company motivational program. I do not believe you need a brass band to try to buy atmosphere for motivation. A planned incentive program which is understood by everyone in the company will prove to be the greatest continuing motivator. Individual 'personal quality, value, and integrity charts' are a very effective motivating tool which I recommend highly. The attainable upper and lower control limits should be established by the quality assurance organization. Indoctrination and orientation sessions should be conducted for all management and personnel, for a clear understanding of the planned program prior to formal installation. This must be a total impact program. This must be a management program with full management support in every respect. I believe and recommend that management must take the initiative by showing their personnel that 'management cares' and that 'management is interested' in their personnel. Management interest and concern for attaining quality, value, cost reduction, safety, service, and integrity will prove to be another great continuing motivator in the program. Management and personnel at all levels will respond to a well planned program with administrative leadership. The program must be administered, otherwise, it will fall apart and may never get off the ground. Plan it well and follow the plan.

The art and science of producing reliable parts and equipment using 'special processes' requires well-trained, qualified, and motivated people who are capable of and can demonstrate their ability prior to producing a product for sale to commercial, industrial, military, marine, scientific or space oriented customers.

It doesn't cost any more money to produce reliable, quality products than it does to produce questionable, poor quality products. In fact, it will cost more in the end to produce the poor quality because of the rework, test failures, trouble shooting time, misuse and abuse of tools, and possible destruction of equipment. We all must agree and acknowledge the basic fact that the cost effective way to operate is to DO IT RIGHT THE FIRST TIME!

All personnel assume a role of responsibility with regard to the quality and reliability of the finished product. Only through training, motivation, and qualification can high quality and consistency of workmanship be built into the product. The design engineer must design the quality and reliability into the product. The inspector cannot 'inspect' quality and reliability into the product. All personnel must understand what he or she is doing, and by this we mean they must comprehend and know their job function, how it's done, and all the proper tools, methods, and techniques employed to DO THE JOB RIGHT THE FIRST TIME.

A concerted training, motivation, and qualification program, tailored to the operation of the organization, will provide qualified personnel who have demonstrated their ability to build products or provide supplies of acceptable quality assurance workmanship standards and specifications, thus giving management a high degree of confidence in each person as an individual who will make up the first line quality team for . . . QUALITY-RELIABILITY-VALUE-SAFETY-SERVICE-INTEGRITY.

Specific 'special process' programs are contained in our 'quality assurance workmanship standards manual' which is recommended for universal use by commercial, industrial, military, space, marine, scientific, educational, and governmental organizations for achieving high level quality, value, and integrity.

Signing pledge cards 'to do my best' is one method used in motivation programs. However, I would rather rely on the employees' understanding the motivation program. I would rather rely on effective communications and acknowledging a job well done at the time it is done and via a well administered employee communication program. This technique would utilize eye catching posters in frames, along with large banners promoting quality, value, cost and scrap reduction, safety and integrity, placed in strategic locations; pocket savers with posters which I call "walking motivators"; bulletin boards; communication stations; company newspapers; commercially available brochures; and many other items which can be used cost effectively to keep quality, value, cost and scrap reduction, safety, and integrity before their eyes wherever they go. Again, this is a sales program. Compare it to selling toothpaste. Companies wouldn't sell much tooth paste if they didn't advertise and keep their product before the public on a continuing basis. The same principle applies here. You are selling and motivating your people to produce consistent acceptable quality in everything they do. Just remember one thing, the program must be a management program backed by the entire management team. The program will then be a personal motivation program for management and personnel which will be self-sustaining because everyone understands, everyone cares, and everyone is on the team.

A special part of any program is communicating effectively with every person. This applies particularly to the corrective action and awareness stage of the program. The individual must always be kept informed as to mistakes or problems being found. Please be sure to go over mistakes and problems with the individual on a personal basis. If he or she has made a mistake, take it to them immediately so proper corrective action can be taken. This is a vital part of training and motivation. Your program should allow you to trace the problem to the individual. This is one of the greatest personal motivating forces—their name, initials, stamp, or other identifying means should be on their work or the tag identifying the work to the person.

Use the personal commitment tool of your name on your work which means the job is complete and you did the job right the first time. Talk Quality, think Quality, produce Quality, sell Quality.

Your total impact program will assist you in achieving your total quality management and personnel team.

I believe in incentives and goals. You can use a monetary incentive for achieving goals or items of a personal nature, such as writing pens, lighters, pins, plaques, fishing trips, vacations, or other suitable incentives. Sometimes, the greatest incentive a person can ask for is a personal thank you from the boss. I always recommend that approach. These are suggestions; you use whatever will do the best job for you.

The Motivation Challenge

As quality-minded people, you are the V.I.P., the "Vitally Interested Person". You, as the professional engineer or as the professional manufacturing manager, have the responsibility for motivating management and personnel via quality awareness programs—and most important—through your outstanding prformance in a professional capacity within your organization. **Motivating Management and Personnel for Quality Improvement is your business.** Making quality products at maximum profits is your business. Quality, Reliability, Value, Safety, Service, and Integrity are your business and thus become your personal challenge.

M — Money	M — Manpower	P — Planner
O — Others	A — Art	E — Engineer
T — Time	N — National	O — Organizer
I — Integrity	A — Attitude	P — Programmer
V — Value	G — Greatness	L — Leader
A — Acceptable	E — Efficient	E — Entrepreneur
T — Teamwork	M — Materials	
I — Interest	E — Effective	
N — Natural	N — Numbers	
G — Guidance	T — Talent	

F — First	Q — Quantity
O — Opportunity	U — Understand
R — Reliability	A — Ability
	L — Learn
	I — Inspect
	T — Test
	Y — You

—Motivating Management People for Quality !—

People are your most important asset for motivating management. Management needs you. Management wants professional quality people who are Product, Program, and Personnel Experts. Accept the challenge and be ready to motivate management and personnel for quality improvement.

TYPICAL MOTIVATION MATERIAL

BILLBOARD DISPLAY

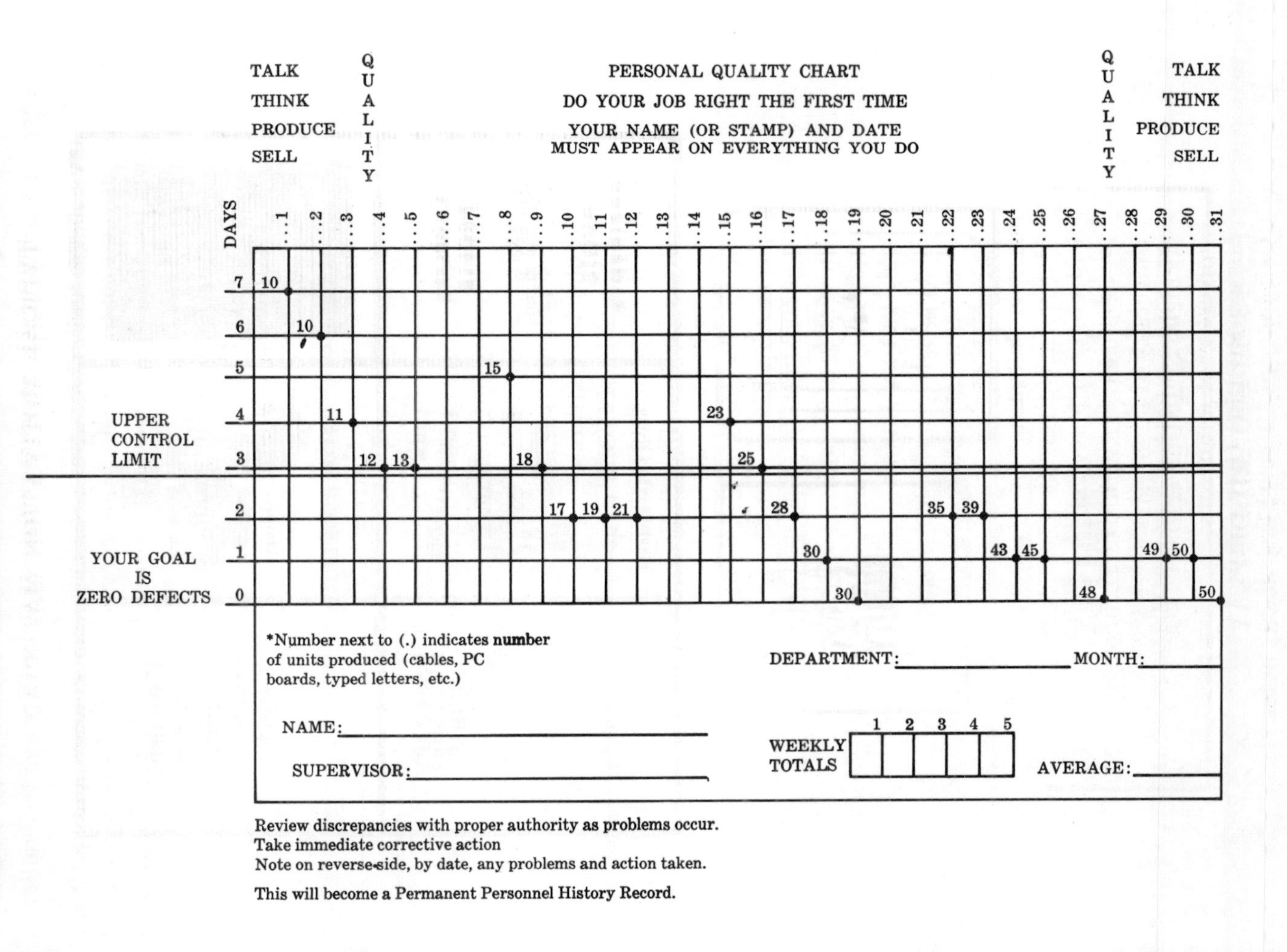
TALK
THINK
PRODUCE
SELL
QUALITY
PERSONAL QUALITY CHART
DO YOUR JOB RIGHT THE FIRST TIME
YOUR NAME (OR STAMP) AND DATE
MUST APPEAR ON EVERYTHING YOU DO
QUALITY
TALK
THINK
PRODUCE
SELL
DAYS
...1
...2
...3
...4
...5
...6
...7
...8
...9
..10
..11
..12
..13
..14
..15
..16
..17
..18
..19
..20
..21
..22
..23
..24
..25
..26
..27
..28
..29
..30
..31
7
6
5
4
3
2
1
0
UPPER
CONTROL
LIMIT
YOUR GOAL
IS
ZERO DEFECTS
10
10
11
12
13
15
18
17
19
21
23
25
28
30
30
35
39
43
45
48
49
50
50
*Number next to (.) indicates **number** of units produced (cables, PC boards, typed letters, etc.)
DEPARTMENT:
MONTH:
NAME:
SUPERVISOR:
WEEKLY
TOTALS
1
2
3
4
5
AVERAGE:
Review discrepancies with proper authority **as problems occur.**
Take immediate corrective action
Note on reverse-side, by date, any problems and action taken.
This will become a Permanent Personnel History Record.

Colleges and Universities Presenting Courses on Quality and Reliability

Many colleges and universities present special courses and seminars as a part of their continuing education services. Some of the schools are well known for their quality efforts. The following is furnished as a partial list.

Arizona State University
Auburn University
University of Baltimore
Baylor University
Bradley University
Brigham Young University
Butler University
University of California in Los Angeles
Carnegie Institute of Technology
University of Cincinnati
Clemson University
Coe College
Columbia University
University of Connecticut
University of Dayton
Drury College (Breech School of Business)
Fenn College
George Washington University
Georgia Tech
Hartford State Technology Institute
University of Hawaii
University of Houston
University of Illinois
Illinois Institute of Technology
Iowa State University
LaFayette College
Loyola-Baltimore
Marquette University
University of Maryland
Massachusetts Institute of Technology
University of Michigan
Michigan State University
University of Minnesota
Mississippi State University
University of Missouri Extension Center

Colleges and Universities (Continued)

Missouri School of Mines and Metallurgy
Mohawk Valley Community College
University of Nebraska
City College of New York
New York University
University of North Carolina
North Carolina State University
Northwestern University
Ohio Mechanics Institute
Municipal University of Omaha
Orange Coast College
Oregon State University
University of Pennsylvania—Wharton School of Business
Penn State University
Philadelphia College of Textile and Science
University of Pittsburgh
Princeton University
Purdue University
Purdue University—Calumet
University of Richmond
University of Rochester
Rock Valley College, Rockford, Illinois
Rutgers University
St. Louis University
University of Southern California
Stevens Institute of Technology
University of Tennessee
Texas A. & M. University
University of Texas at Arlington
University of Toledo
Virginia Polytechnical Institute
University of Washington
Wayne State University
Western Michigan University
University of Wisconsin
University of Wisconsin—Milwaukee
Worcester Junior College
Stanford University
Texas Christian University—Fort Worth, Texas

Master's Degree in Quality Control

University of Dallas
3113 University Avenue
Irving, Texas 75060
(214) 253-1123

Associate Degree in Quality Control

Daytona Beach Junior College
Loomis and Lockhart Streets
Daytona Beach, Florida

Triton College
1000 Wolf Road
Northlake, Illinois

Laney College
1001 Third Avenue
Oakland, California

San Diego Junior College
835 Twelfth Avenue
San Diego, California

Rock Valley College
Rockford, Illinois

De Anza and Foothill Colleges
San Francisco Bay Area
California

Brevard Junior College
Cape Canaveral, Florida

Muskegon County Community College
Vanderlaan Branch
Muskegon, Michigan

Ohio Mechanics Institute
1104 Walnut Street
Cincinnati, Ohio

Pierce College
6201 Winnetka Avenue
Woodland Hills, California

Associate Degree (Continued)

San Diego City College
1425 Russ Boulevard
San Diego, California

Temple University Technical Institute
Broad Street and Columbus Avenue
Philadelphia, Pennsylvania

Wayne State University
640 Temple Street
Detroit, Michigan

CERTIFIED QUALITY ENGINEER

A Professional Certificate granted by:

The American Society for Quality Control, Inc.
161 West Wisconsin Avenue
Milwaukee, Wisconsin 53203

for professional attainment in Quality Engineering. Professional status achieved by time, experience, training, and tests, as conducted by ASQC.

TYPICAL PROFESSIONAL SOCIETIES, COURSES SEMINARS AND PUBLICATIONS

American Society for Quality Control, Inc. (ASQC)
Education and Training Institute
161 West Wisconsin Avenue
Milwaukee, Wisconsin 53203
(414) 272-8575

- Quality Control Engineering
- Fundamentals of Reliability
- Management of Quality Costs
- Product Quality Auditing
- Management of the Inspection Function
- Annual Technical Conference Training Courses and Technical Papers
- ASQC Divisions and Sections present courses and seminars
- Publication: "Quality Progress"

American Management Association (AMA)
135 West 50th Street

AUTHOR	TITLE	PUBLISHER
Fisher, R. A.	Design of Experiments	Hafner
Fisher, R. A.	Contributions to Mathematical Statistics	Wiley
Goulden	Methods of Statistical Analysis	Wiley
Grant, E. L.	Statistical Quality Control	McGraw-Hill
Hansen, B.	Quality Control	Prentice-Hall
Hald, A.	Statistical Theory with Engineering Applications	Wiley
Hald, A.	Statistical Tables and Formulas	Wiley
Hicks, C. R.	Fundamental Concepts in the Design of Experiments	Holt, Rinehart and Winston
Hoel	Introduction of Mathematical Statistics	Wiley
Hotelling, H.	Techniques of Statistical Analysis	McGraw-Hill
Ireson, W. G.	Reliability Handbook	McGraw-Hill
Juran, J.	Quality Control Handbook	McGraw-Hill
Kempthorne	The Design and Analysis of Experiments	Wiley
Kendall, M. G.	Advance Theory of Statistics, Vol. 1 and 2	C. Griffin & Co., Ltd.
Lindgren and McElrath	Introduction to Probability and Statistics	Mac Millan Co.
Lloyd and Lipow	Reliability: Management, Methods, and Mathematics	Prentice Hall
MIL-STD-105	Sampling Procedures and Tables for Inspection by Attributes	U.S. Printing Office
Peach, P.	Quality Control for Management	Prentice Hall
Rice	Control Charts	Wiley
Scheffe, H.	Analysis of Variance	Wiley
Shewhart, W. A.	Economic Control of Quality of Manufactured Products	Van Nostrand
Smedecar, G. W.	Statistical Methods	Iowa State College
Stiles, E. M.	Handbook for Total Quality Assurance	Prentice Hall
Stok, Th. L.	The Worker and Quality Control	Univ. of Michigan
Western Electric	Statistical Quality Control Handbook	Western Electric
Wallis and Roberts	Statistics	Free Press
Wald	Sequential Analysis	Wiley
Wald	Statistical Decision Functions	Wiley
Youden	Statistical Methods for Chemists	Wiley

ADDITIONAL PUBLICATIONS

American Society for Training and Development	Training and Development Handbook	McGraw-Hill
Publisher	Quality Assurance Magazine	Hitchcock Publishing Co.
Publisher	Quality Register	Hitchcock Publishing Co.
Publisher	Training in Business and Industry	Gellert Publishing Co.
United States of America Standards Institute	A Catalog of Publications and Standards	U.S.A.S.I., New York City

The Quality Alphabet From A to Z

A Attitude; Assurance; Acceptable; Attributes; Audit; Analysis; Appraisal; Action
B Built-in; Budget; Before; Buyer
C Communicate; Control; Coordinate; Cooperate; Complete; Compliance; Customers; Costs; Calibration; Configuration
D Detect; Delivery; Defect; Data; Design; Documentation
E Excellence; Everyone; Education; Engineering; Equipment; Economic; Effective
F Finest; First; Flow; Failure; Facilities; Feed-back; Function
G Good; Goals; Graphs; Guarantee
H Housekeeping; Hardware; Handling; Hazard; Homogeneous; Human-factors
I Integrity; Interest; Inspect; Incentive; Improvements; Information; Internal
J Justification; Jointly
K Knowledge
L Liability; Learn; Loyal; Legal; Level; Limits; Lot; Life; Laboratory; Loss; Logistics
M Management; Money; Motivation; Material; Manufacturing; Machines; Manpower; Maintain
N Normal; Natural; National Bureau of Standards
O Optimum; On-time; Office; Organization; Objectives; Operator; Operation; Output
P Profit; Price; Procedures; Program; People; Project; Personnel; Professional; Plan; Prevention; Process; Problems; Purchasing
Q Quantity; Quality; Quickly; Qualify
R Reliability; Reasonable; Repeat; Records; Responsibility; Receive; Random; Reports
S Safety; Service; Satisfaction; Simplicity; Standards; Sample; Survey; System; Schedule; Statistics; Surveillance
T Test; Together; Training; Time; Talent; Traceable
U Universal; Unified; Understand; Use; Upper-limits
V Value; Volume; Variable; Variance; Verification; Vendor; Vendee
W Workmanship; Warranty; Wear-out
X X-ray; X-Bar Charts
Y You; You; You
Z Zero-defects

From Attitude . . . To Motivation . . . To Zero Defects

YOU are Always Involved in

The Control and Assurance of Quality

Chapter 4

ENGINEERING, MANAGEMENT, AND PERSONNEL

The quality and Value Engineering effort must begin on a side-by-side basis with design, project or program engineering functions. We must put our dollars "Up Front" in the Planning, Engineering and Prevention stages for designed-in Quality, Reliability, Value, Safety, Service and Product Integrity. We must stay "Up Front" all the way, for Cost Reductions, Product, Production and Profit Improvement. We must do everything possible to Do the Job Right the First Time, for maximum Quality, Reliability and Value at the lowest cost. We must all realize that we are all on the same Management Quality Team, and everything we do must enhance the organization with which we are associated, as related to Profit, Loyalty and Dedicated Service.

Quality Organizations will differ from company to company, because no two companies are alike. In fact, large companies with many operating divisions often appear to be separate companies. This is quite common in Industry and Business today and, in many cases, the "Independent Operating Division" is quite successful. It is difficult to argue with success in these instances, and about all we can say is that the company could be **More Successful** and make **More Profit** with a Unified and Coordinated Corporate Quality Team. I endorse this philosophy and recommend this approach for uniform Standardization, Flexibility of Personnel, and maximum Communication, Coordination and Cooperation at all levels. Based on personal experience, I can truly illustrate this point as follows: I have been associated with a major company having four operating divisions in four different sections of our country. By having uniform standardization in all divisions, i.e., (same general physical layout, same colors, same furniture, same general policies, procedures and Quality Standards), it provided maximum flexibility and use of personnel on a corporate basis for the good of the company. Personnel could be transferred from one division to another with little or no down time or readjustment cycle. Products could be sold or sent from division to division with minimum effort, based on Unified Policies, Procedures, Specifications and Workmanship Standards. A second illustration can be made with reference to the Bell Telephone Organization. The Bell Telephone Laboratories create and design the telephone equipment that the Western Electric Organizations produce for the Bell System. I can safely say that you can walk into different Bell Telephone Company central offices and find the telephone equipment, as manufactured and installed by Western Electric, to be literally the same in like offices, because the Specifications and Standards are the same. Flexibility of Personnel is built-in. Installers can be transferred around the country. You and I can travel the country and use Bell System Equipment with little or no learning or adjustment cycle. This Management, Personnel and Customer Philosophy works. It is cost effective and profitable. It produces products and services of uniform Quality, Reliability, Value and Integrity.

Talented Engineers must design Quality, Reliability, Value, Safety, Service and Integrity into the product. Talented Quality, Reliability, Value, Safety and Service Engineers must assist the Design Engineer in achieving his design goals. Talented Manufacturing Engineers and qualified, trained Production Personnel must build the products with Quality, Reliability, Value, Safety, Service and Integrity. Talented sales and marketing personnel must promote and sell the quality products with integrity. The customer must insist on and receive quality products and services.

However, we find ourselves in a rather serious set of circumstances, based on a continual shortage of qualified engineers, managers, and manufacturing talent. We must realize that our colleges and universities are not graduating quality engineers, reliability engineers, or value engineers. We must realize that many, many colleges do not understand quality, reliability, and value engineering, nor do they recognize these as professional and scientific subject matter to be taught to their students. The various individual professional societies, such as American Society for Quality Control, Society of American Value Engineers and their world-wide members, are slowly making progress in educating the educators to recognize the vital need for producing engineers, managers, and manufacturing personnel who are professionals in the technical, scientific, and management fields of quality, reliability, and value engineering. We need professional quality assurance engineers and managers who are 'management engineers' majoring in quality, reliability, and value. Courses are now being generated in a few colleges and universities. We have a long way to go. We must achieve our goal of having required courses in quality, reliability, and value in all colleges and universities as mandatory for all male and female students with appropriate provisions made for students to major in these fields for Bachelor and Masters Degrees. I would encourage female students to enter these professional fields. The professional quality field is wide open to men and women. Some very high quality and reliability positions in major industries are held by women. Girls, the opportunities are there for you if you want and like the work. There are no barriers to race, color, or any other factors. All you need is personal drive, interest, dedication, and education.

I have constant requests from nation-wide companies in all fields of endeavor for young engineers with knowledge and/or experience in Quality, Reliability and Manufacturing, to name a few. In this day and age of Science, Engineering, Education and Management, I find it rather ridiculous to have to say that most college students are completely unaware of the professional opportunities available in Quality Assurance, Reliability and associated positions.

I have often been asked, "What is a Quality Engineer?" or, "What is a Reliability Engineer?" and, "What do they do?" Based on every company being different with regard to People, Products, Program and Organization structure, I must state that we must first qualify the Industry and Product to determine the need. For example: a Chemical firm may want a Quality Engineer with a Bachelor of Science Degree in Chemistry for a particular position in Process Quality Control, with specific duties concerned with conducting Process Capability Studies; instituting Process Control Charts; and utilizing Statistical Sampling Techniques: Salary: $11,000.00 up. An Electronic Manufacturing Company may want a Reliability Engineer with a Bachelor of Science, Electrical Engineering Degree, to conduct Reliability Predictions; Reliability Circuit and Component Analysis; Failure Mode and Effect Analysis; with knowledge of Engineering Computer Techniques: Salary: $14,000.00 up. An Aerospace firm may want a Quality Assurance Manager with a degree in Industrial Management, to establish a documented and functioning program for the Control and Assurance of Quality and Reliability, from Engineering through Customer Acceptance; Vendor Quality Assurance experience; Customer Contact and Contract Negotiation experience being necessary; along with complete working knowledge of Quality and Reliability Specifications: Salary: $18,000.00 up.

These three typical examples indicate a cross section of some of the requirements I see in our office from nation-wide firms. You will notice that each position requires a degree. This is mandatory in some cases, but unnecessary in many other cases. I firmly believe that it is a crime to refuse to consider a qualified and experienced individual, who can fill the position in every respect, because he does not have a degree. I know that we are wasting manpower, and not utilizing available talent to the greatest extent possible. Some companies will not review or consider non-degreed people. However, they will constantly complain of Personnel Shortages and miss schedules, because they will not consider Qualified and Experienced talent. This is unwise and costly management. We must constantly strive for the Right Person for the Job, regardless of circumstances. Management should be "Result" oriented, rather than "Degree Ratio" minded.

Management and their Personnel Departments should concern themselves with establishing realistic job specifications which are 'people oriented,' to achieve a successful marriage between the person and the position. If this were accomplished, we could utilize our manpower with remarkable results. I have included some typical job descriptions in this book to acquaint you with how they are written and what they contain. They include: Quality Assurance Manager; Quality Control Supervisor; Quality Planning and Engineering Supervisor; Quality Engineer; Assistant Quality Engineer; Quality Control Foreman; Chemical-Metallurgical Engineer; Calibration Specialist.

As a professional quality engineer, I do not like to see waste of any kind, whether it be manpower, time, material, or money. In your capacity as an engineer, manager, salesman, administrator, Production Technician or Student, your interest should be in achieving your Personal Plan for Progress and Success. By working to your Personal Plan, you should strive at all times to do whatever you do Right the First Time, At the Lowest Cost, On Time, with Excellence of Quality, Value, and Unquestionable Integrity.

Today, we are all faced with serious Management and Personnel Problems in all areas of business and industry. The problems will not be any better tomorrow, next week, next month, nor next year. In fact, the problems will multiply and we will become more frustrated unless we approach new avenues to achieve progress and success. One of the new professional and scientific approaches to Management and Personnel Selection, Placement, Training, and Development is the "Art and Science of Graphoanalysis." This science of Professional Handwriting Analysis is being used more and more by Business and Industry because of the Personal Characteristic approach to the Individual, as an individual. A Graphoanalysis Study of the individual's handwriting shows where the strong and weak spots are and allows for an "up-Front Personal Plan" to be developed for individual managers and personnel. We use the team approach, with a Certified Master Graphoanalyst; an Educational and Vocational Psychologist; and a Management and Personnel Consultant. The combined talents provide a solid base for the search, selection, and placement of management and personnel for our clients under Search Contract Agreements.

There is much interest in the Science of Graphoanalysis and a great deal can be said about the subject as a "Personal Approach for Solving Management and Personnel Problems." I would recommend the Training Courses being given by Professional Certified Graphoanalysis Experts as a means of obtaining the Theory, Application, and Professional Handwriting Techniques as used for individual development, personnel selection, and for vocational and career guidance. The old and new Professional Managers and Professional Personnel People should be vitally interested in Graphoanalysis for Management and Personnel Selection and Development.

Although specific training programs for manufacturing and associated personnel are covered in our "Quality Assurance Workmanship Standards Manual," I would like to briefly cover a Training, Orientation, and Motivation Program which is badly needed in Business and Industry. This could be called a "This is Your Company" or "What's Going On" program for new and old Engineers, Managers, and Personnel. This is an orientation and indoctrination program. The theme should be Communication, Coordination, and Cooperation. The program should start with the Personnel Department, for this is where you can gain or lose good people for the organization. There are entirely too many misinformed, unknowledgable personnel departments. Those of you who have helped to develop organizations and who have had to work with and through unskilled personnel departments, realize how frustrating your job can be. This is particularly highlighted by personal experience with some Professional Personnel Department people who were looking for people they wouldn't recognize if they had interviewed them for 2 hours. This is created by poor communication, poor indoctrination, and poor administration. The Personnel Department did not "understand" what they were looking for. They could not be specific. They could not tell you what they wanted. They could not communicate. Please stop for a moment and try to recall the Personnel Departments that you know of, who do not, cannot, or will not communicate. This is a common Personnel Department Problem. Too many good Engineers, Managers, Executives, and operating personnel are lost to your competition due to Personnel Department Communication Problems. Some causes are: Lost applications and resumes; no follow up; conflicting stories; too long in processing; a high and mighty attitude by companies and Personnel Departments; too busy to communicate, coordinate, and cooperate to name a few common causes. I know of too many cases where the individual department manager or executive has stated, "We cannot fool with our personnel department any longer. We will recruit and obtain our own people and then advise the personnel department to complete the paper work and process the individual." This is not good and should serve to inspire Personnel Departments to develop themselves as professionals and to utilize all professional avenues of obtaining qualified management and personnel for their companies.

As new Engineering personnel join the company, I would recommend a Training and Orientation period in the Manufacturing and Quality Departments. This will pay larger dividends later on because the New Engineer will "know and understand what manufacturing can and cannot do;—what tolerances they can hold, what equipment the company has, etc." All of this knowledge plays an important part in obtaining "Realistic Design" from your Design Engineers. Why waste 3 months designing something you cannot produce? Why have your design engineers specify tolerances your manufacturing department cannot accomplish? I just want to assure you that these things are happening every day in most every company. I think it is time for you to establish an Up-Front Program for Communication, Coordination, and Cooperation. A simple "Awareness Program" can cost so little and save so much for everyone in the company. By having a "What's Going On Around You" program, the company can probably pay for the entire program on savings realized from decreased "duplication of work based on a lack of communication." In other words, employee A was doing the same job as employee B, because A did not know what B was doing. The morale of management and personnel is of vital importance. An "Awareness Program" can do wonders for everyone's morale. Make sure the Quality Manager has a key spot in your orientation and awareness program. All engineers, managers, and personnel should meet and hear about quality on their first day with the company. Start everyone off on the right foot with a "Think Quality Attitude."

Every company and organization, regardless of size, can and should have a Training and Orientation Program. What you call the program is secondary. I have given several suggestions for your consideration. The need should be evident. Start your Up-Front Training and Orientation Program **now** for amazing cost effective results.

TYPICAL
ORIENTATION AND INDOCTRINATION PROGRAM

TIME: One Hour—first day of employment or as prearranged for old employees.

PLACE: Training room or quiet office

EQUIPMENT: Flip chart; 16mm movie projector and screen; 35 mm slide projector; and accessories such as:
- Display of company products
- Time clock (if used)
- Forms, as normally used
- Specific items of interest or use
- Movies of company, company products
- Quality motivation film

PROGRAM LEADERS:
- Training Director
- Industrial Relations Manager
- Personnel Manager
- Quality Assurance Director or Manager
- Engineering Manager
- Manufacturing Manager
- Plus, any others whose participation may be vital to the orientation program.

REMEMBER: First impressions are often lasting impressions. This is an important program. People are your most important asset.

PROGRAM CONTENT:
1. Introduction of key management and personnel
2. Flip chart of company operation
3. Brief talk by department managers
   THEME: Communicate, Coordinate, Cooperate
   Training—Motivation
   Quality—Integrity
   Housekeeping—Safety, etc.
4. Movie on company, if available

5. Movie or slides on company products
6. Quality motivation film as presented and discussed by Quality Manager, stressing 'do it right the first time' program within the company.
7. Importance of teamwork—how the team functions—desired results
8. Questions and answers
9. Review significant items
10. Welcome to the company—and to our quality team.

TYPICAL
JOB DESCRIPTION

"QUALITY ASSURANCE MANAGER"
Quality Assurance Division

QUALIFICATIONS: Professional Q.C.—Q.A. experience in like or related industry is a prerequisite. A Certified Professional Quality Engineer as qualified by the American Society for Quality Control would be preferred. The experience factor is of prime importance with guidelines from 5 to 20 years or more. A college or university education is highly desirable with either a B.S. or B.A. Degree in engineering, business, industrial management, or equivalent technical fields. Outstanding experience may be considered in lieu of degree if two years of college is completed and experience ranges from 10 to 20 years or more. Managerial-Supervisory experience is a prerequisite in equivalent and/or lower levels of management in such positions as Quality Planning and Engineering Supervisor; Quality Control Supervisor; Quality Assurance Supervisor; Quality Engineering Manager; Vendor Quality Assurance Manager, plus other related positions. Age is not a critical factor based on the above consistent with strong personal characteristics such as drive, determination, enthusiasm, and the will to succeed with a good management and personnel team. The person must be well versed in all areas of quality from receipt of contract to delivery of acceptable products and services. The person must present a good appearance and be capable of maintaining personal contact with customers, vendors, and all levels of company management and personnel. The person must be promotable to higher levels of management and willing to increase in stature through continuous learning via formal advanced education, seminars, and self-education.

GOALS: Personal goals should include promotion to Vice President-Director of Q.A. and Reliability; Vice President and General Manager and/or other corporate level positions.

RESPONSIBILITIES:

1. Responsible for total Quality Assurance Division, which includes all Quality Control functions, i.e., Receiving Inspection, In-Process Inspection, Final Inspection, Pack and Shipping Inspection, and all Quality Planning and Engineering functions, i.e., Program Plans, Inspection and Quality Engineering Procedures, Vendor rating and analysis, calibration laboratory, Chemical-Metallurgical Laboratory, Material Review Board, Data Analysis and reporting, etc.
2. Reports to the Vice President-Director of Quality Assurance and Reliability.
3. Manage and direct the cost-effective operations of the total Q.A. Division as prescribed by the Vice President-Director of Q. and R. consistent with meeting and/or exceeding management goals for costs, quality, delivery, schedules, and profit.
4. Guide, manage, direct, and supervise engineers, analysts, technicians, coordinators, supervisors, general foremen, foremen, assistant foremen, inspectors, and clerical personnel.
5. Originate and maintain necessary controls to follow plans, programs, procedures, and company policies.
6. Division planning—short and long range.
7. Establish manpower and capital budgets, necessary controls, and approve expenditures.
8. Recruit personnel in conjunction with industrial relations and search firms.
9. Interview, hire, and/or terminate personnel for cause.
10. Evaluate personnel for merit increases and promotions.
11. Train and motivate personnel and management at all levels of the company.
12. Prepare your people and yourself to be promoted.
13. Personal and business conduct shall be of unquestionable integrity.
14. Command and maintain the professional respect of management, personnel, vendors, and the customers.
15. Participate in professional societies for company and personal growth.
16. Maintain clean working areas and environment for efficient work by all personnel.

RESPONSIBILITES: (cont'd)

17. Communicate—Coordinate—Cooperate with all levels of management, personnel, vendors, and customers.

TYPICAL
JOB DESCRIPTION

"QUALITY CONTROL SUPERVISOR"
Quality Assurance Division

QUALIFICATIONS: Professional Q.C.—Q.A. experience in like or related industry is a prerequisite. A Certified Professional Quality Engineer as qualified by the American Society for Quality Control would be preferred. The experience factor is of prime importance with guidelines set from 5 to 20 years or more. A college or university graduate with a B.S. or B.A. Degree would be preferred but is not mandatory if high school, technical trade school, and work experience is sufficient to offset or equal the college education. Supervisory—managerial experience is a prerequisite in equivalent and/or lower levels of management in such positions as Assistant Foreman, Foreman, General Foreman, Supervisor, Manager, etc., in like or related industrial fields of work. Age is not a critical factor based on the above consistent with strong personal characteristics such as drive, determination, enthusiasm, and the will to succeed with a good management and personnel team. The person must be well versed in all areas of quality from receipt of contract to delivery of acceptable products and services. The person must present a good appearance and be capable of maintaining personal contact with customers, vendors, and all levels of company management and personnel. The person must be promotable to higher levels of management and willing to increase in stature through continuous learning via formal education, seminars, and self-education.

GOALS: Personal goals should include promotion to Quality Assurance Manager; and Vice President-Director of Quality Assurance and Reliability, through outstanding performance.

RESPONSIBILITIES:

1. Responsible for quality control section, including receiving inspection, all in-process inspection (line insp.—mechanical insp.—process insp.), final inspection, pack and shipping inspection, etc.
2. Reports directly to the Quality Assurance Manager.
3. Manage and direct the cost-effective operations of the Q.C. Section

RESPONSIBILITIES: (cont'd)

as prescribed by the Q.A. Manager and the Vice President-Director of Quality Assurance and Reliability, to meet or exceed management goals for costs, quality, schedules, and profit.

4. Guide, direct, and supervise General Foremen, Foremen, Assistant Foremen, Supervisors, Inspectors, and clerical personnel.
5. Originate and maintain necessary control to follow procedures, specifications, and company policies.
6. Establish budgets and necessary controls.
7. Hire and/or terminate personnel, as required to do the job—or for cause.
8. Train and motivate personnel at all levels of the organization.
9. Evaluate personnel for merit increases and promotions.
10. Maintain and conduct company and personal business in a manner that will command respect for a person of unquestionable integrity.
11. Participate in professional societies for company and personal growth.
12. Short and long range planning.
13. Maintain clean working areas and environment for efficient work by all personnel.
14. Communicate—Coordinate—Cooperate with all levels of management, personnel, vendors, and customers.

TYPICAL
JOB DESCRIPTION

"QUALITY PLANNING AND ENGINEERING SUPERVISOR"
Quality Assurance Division

QUALIFICATIONS: Professional Quality Control—Quality Assurance experience in like or related industry is a prerequisite. A Certified Professional Quality Engineer as qualified by the American Society for Quality Control would be preferred. The experience factor is of prime importance with guidelines from 5 to 20 years or more. A college or university education with a B.S. or B.A. Degree in Engineering, Business, Industrial Management, Mathematics, Physics, Education, or equivalent technical fields. Outstanding experience may be considered in lieu of degree if 2 years of college is completed and experience ranges from 10 to 20 years or more. Supervisory/Managerial experience is a prerequisite in equivalent and/or lower levels of management in such positions as Quality, Plans and Programs Supervisor, Manager, Engineer, Vendor Quality Assurance Manager, Quality Engineering Manager, Laboratory

Supervisor, Supervisor—Data Analysis and Reporting, plus other related positions. Age is not a critical factor based on the above consistent with strong personal characteristics such as drive, determination, enthusiasm, and the will to succeed with a good management and personnel team. The person must be well versed in all areas of Quality from receipt of contract to delivery of acceptable products. The person must present a good appearance and be capable of maintaining personal contact with customers, vendors, and all levels of company management and personnel. The person must be promotable to higher levels of management and willing to increase in stature through continuous learning via formal education, seminars and self-education.

GOALS: Personal goals should include promotion to Quality Assurance Manager and Corporate Director of Quality Assurance and Reliability through outstanding performance.

RESPONSIBILITIES:

1. Responsible for Quality Planning and Engineering Department which includes program plans, engineering and procedures, vendor rating and analysis, calibration and process control laboratory, Material Review Board, Data Analysis and Rating.
2. Reports directly to the Division Quality Assurance Manager.
3. Manage and direct the cost effective operations of the Quality Planning and Engineering Department as prescribed by the Quality Assurance Manager and the Corporate Director of Quality Assurance and Reliability to meet or exceed management goals for costs, quality, schedules, and profit.
4. Guide, direct, and supervise engineers, analysts, technicians, coordinators, supervisors, Assistant Quality Engineers, and clerical personnel.
5. Short and long range planning.
6. Originate and maintain necessary control to establish and follow procedures, specifications, company policies.
7. Establish budgets and necessary controls.
8. Hire and/or terminate personnel, as required to do the job, or for cause.
9. Train and motivate personnel at all levels of the organization.
10. Evaluate personnel for merit increases and promotions.
11. Prepare your people and yourself to be promoted.
12. Maintain and conduct personal and business life to command the professional respect of management, personnel and the customers,

RESPONSIBILITIES: (cont'd)

as being a person of unquestionable integrity.

13. Participate in professional societies for company and personal growth.
14. Maintain clean working areas and environment for efficient work by all personnel.

TYPICAL
JOB DESCRIPTION

"QUALITY ENGINEER"
Quality Assurance Division

QUALIFICATIONS: Professional Quality Control—Quality Assurance experience in a like or related industry is a prerequisite. A Certified Professional Quality Engineer as qualifed by the American Society for Quality Control is preferred. A college or university education is highly desirable, with a B.S. or B.A. Degree in engineering, business, industrial management, mathematics, physics, education, or equivalent technical fields. Outstanding experience may be considered in lieu of a degree if two years of college is complete, the person is attending college, and experience ranges from 2 to 20 years or more. Knowledge and background in writing detailed inspection procedures; determining inspection methods; reviewing procurement documents and establshing quality requirements; contract evaluation for quality/reliability requirements; evaluating specifications and drawings for sound quality engineering action and/or disposition; working understanding of manufacturing methods, machines, tools, processes, finishes; quality systems, program plans, and procedures; vendor rating and analysis; calibration and process controls; Material Review Board functions—actions and dispositions; data analysis and reporting; vendor surveys—professional evaluation and analysis. Age is not a critical factor, consistent with all of the above, coupled with the strong desire and willingness to succeed and progress within the quality organization and the company. Person must present good appearance, be well versed and capable of meeting and working with all levels of management and personnel, including the vendors and the customers. The person should be promotable to more responsible positions and willing to increase his knowledge through continuous learning via formal education, seminars, and self-education.

GOALS: Promotion to Senior Quality Engineer; Quality Control supervision and management within the company.

RESPONSIBILITIES:

1. Reports to Quality Assurance Management.
2. Writing detailed inspection and quality procedures, control charts, etc.
3. Determine best inspection methods for the job and improve existing methods for time and cost savings.
4. Review procurement documents and prescribe adequate quality requirements.
5. Review contracts for quality and reliability requirements.
6. Review and evaluate engineering drawings and specifications for accuracy.
7. Methods of manufacturing, machines, tools, processes, finishes, and special process controls.
8. Write quality program plans and procedures.
9. Maintain vendor rating and analysis.
10. Maintain calibration system and controls.
11. Material Review Board functions per procedure (function, action, and control).
12. Data analysis and reporting.
13. Vendor surveys—professional evaluation, analysis, rating, and recommendations.
14. Train and motivate personnel.
15. Command professional respect of management and personnel at all levels.
16. Participate in A.S.Q.C. for personal growth and development.
17. Maintain clean work area.
18. Communicate—Coordinate—Cooperate with Management and Personnel.

TYPICAL
JOB DESCRIPTION

"ASSISTANT QUALITY ENGINEER"
Quality Assurance Division

QUALIFICATIONS: Professional Quality Control—Quality Assurance experience in a like or related industry is a desirable prerequisite. A Certified Professional Quality Engineer as qualified by the American Society for Quality Control is preferred. A person working toward this professional level would be acceptable. A college or university education is desirable, with a B.S. or B.A. Degree in engineering, business, industrial management, mathematics, physics, education, or equivalent technical fields. Outstanding experience will be considered in lieu of a degree if one year of college is complete, the person is attending college, and experience ranges from one to ten years or more. Knowledge and background in quality control inspection methods, procedures, and techniques, as well as vendor quality assurance, material review functions and material coordination, basic understanding of manufacturing methods, machines, tools, processes, data analysis, control charts and reporting. Age is not a critical factor, consistent with all the above. Person must be well versed and capable of working with management, personnel, vendors, and customers. The person must present a good appearance and conduct himself in a dignified and respectable manner. The person should be promotable and willing to increase his/her knowledge through continuous learning via formal education, seminars, and self-education.

GOALS: Promotion to Quality Engineer; Senior Quality Engineer and Supervision.

RESPONSIBILITIES:

1. Work under guidance and direction of Quality Engineer and/or group or section manager.
2. Inspection methods and techniques at lowest cost.
3. Write inspection procedures and set up control charts.
4. Maintain vendor rating and analysis.
5. Maintain process control charts and reports.
6. Coordinate MRB material, maintain and control records.
7. Data analysis and reports.
8. Command professional respect of management and personnel.
9. Participate in A.S.Q.C. for personal development.
10. Maintain clean work area.
11. Communicate—Coordinate—Cooperate with Management and Personnel.

TYPICAL
JOB DESCRIPTION

"QUALITY CONTROL FOREMAN"
Quality Assurance Division

QUALIFICATIONS: Professional Q.C.—Q.A. experience in like or related industry is a prerequisite. A Certified Professional Quality Engineer as qualified by the American Society for Quality Control would be preferred. The experience factor is of prime importance with guidelines from 3 to 20 years or more. A college or university education would be preferred, but is not mandatory, if high school, technical trade school, and work experience is sufficient to offset or equal the college education. Supervisory experience is a prerequisite in equivalent and/or lower levels of management in such positions as Foreman, Assistant Foreman, Supervisor, Leadman, etc., in like or related industrial fields of work. Age is not a critical factor, based on the above and consistent with strong personal characteristics such as drive, determination, enthusiasm and the will to succeed with a good management and personnel team. The person must be well versed in Quality Control and Inspection methods and techniques, including, but not limited to, Quality Control Receiving Inspection of all types of commercial, industrial, and military hardware, materials, and equipment; Quality Control in-process inspection methods and techniques in machine shop fabrication, assembly of mechanical products, vehicles, etc.; special process quality control inspection of plating, chemical finishing, painting, non-destructive testing, and related areas of concern; final Quality Control test and inspection; pack and shipping inspection; care and use of inspection tools and gages; calibration; training and motivation of hourly employees. The person must present a good appearance and be capable of maintaining personal contact with all levels of management and personnel. The person should be promotable to higher levels of management, and be willing to increase in stature through continuous learning via formal education, seminars, and self-education.

GOALS: Personal goals should include advancement and promotion to Quality Control Supervisor, Quality Assurance Manager, or other industrial management positions through outstanding performance.

RESPONSIBILITIES:

1. Responsible for one or more of the quality control inspection sections, including, but not limited to, Receiving Inspection; In-Process Inspection (line inspection—mechanical/machine shop—special process inspection); final inspection; pack and shipping inspection, etc.
2. Reports directly to Quality Control Supervisor.
3. Supervise and direct the cost-effective operation of the assigned quality control inspection section as prescribed by the Quality Con-

RESPONSIBILITIES: (cont'd)

trol Supervisor to meet or exceed management goals for costs, quality, schedules, and profit.

4. Guide, direct, and supervise Assistant Foremen, inspection and test personnel.
5. Establish and maintain necessary control to follow procedures, specifications, drawings, and company policies.
6. Assist Quality Control Supervisor in planning manpower and capital budgets.
7. Interview, train, and motivate personnel at all levels of your organization, and maintain discipline and good working relationships.
8. Evaluate personnel for merit increases and promotions.
9. Maintain personal and professional conduct to command respect of management, personnel, and customers.
10. Participate in A.S.Q.C. and other professional societies for company and personal growth.
11. Maintain clean working areas and environment for efficient work by all personnel.
12. Communicate—Coordinate—Cooperate with Management and Personnel.

TYPICAL
JOB DESCRIPTION

"CHEMICAL-METALLURGICAL ENGINEER"
Quality Assurance Division

QUALIFICATIONS: Professional experience in a like or related industry is a prerequisite. A Certified Professional Quality Engineer as qualified by the American Society for Quality Control is preferred. A like certification by chemical and/or metallurgical societies would also be acceptable. A college or university education with a B.S. in chemistry and/or metallurgy. Outstanding experience in directly related work will be considered if degree is in another technical or engineering field, with experience ranging from 5 to 20 years or more in chemical processes and controls, metallurgy of aluminum and steel in all forms. Analysis, evaluation and testing along with trouble-shooting and technical assistance on processes and materials is required. Age is not a critical factor consistent with all of the above, plus the desire and willingness to succeed and progress within the organization and the company. Person must present good appearance, be well versed and capable of meeting and working with all levels of management and personnel, including vendors and the customers. The person should be promotable to more responsible positions and willing to increase his knowledge through continuous learning via formal education, seminars, and self-education. Some supervisory experience is desirable to allow person to supervise laboratory assistants and the total laboratory.

GOALS: Promotion to higher levels of Quality Assurance, Production, or Engineering Management.

RESPONSIBILITIES:

1. Establish, maintain, and supervise chemical-metallurgical laboratory.
2. Establish and maintain control of processes.
3. Analysis, evaluation and testing of metals and chemical processes.
4. Provide technical assistance to operating departments.
5. Technical cognizance of manufacturing methods, processes, finishes, heat treat, et al, for total process controls.
6. Maintain all laboratory records, library and required documents.
7. Train and motivate personnel.
8. Command professional respect of management and personnel at all levels, including vendors and the customers.
9. Maintain clean area and environment for efficient work by all personnel.
10. Establish budgets and necessary controls.
11. Evaluate personnel for merit increases and promotions.
12. Participate in professional societies for company and personal growth.
13. Communicate—Coordinate—Cooperate with Management and Personnel.

TYPICAL
JOB DESCRIPTION

"CALIBRATION SPECIALIST"
Quality Assurance Division

QUALIFICATIONS: Professional experience in calibration and control of all types of mechanical, electro-mechanical, and electrical gages, tools, fixtures and equipment in a like or related industry is a prerequisite. A Certified Professional Quality Engineer as qualified by the American Society for Quality Control would be preferred. A college or university education is desirable but not mandatory. The experience factor is of prime importance with guidelines from 5 to 20 years or more with specific complementary training and education in the field of calibration. Knowledge and background in writing detailed calibration procedures; determining methods; developing new methods and techniques; etc. Fully capable of establishing and maintaining a documented and functioning calibration system and laboratory per specifications such as MIL C-45662. Age is not a critical factor consistent with all of the above and the desire and willingness to succeed and progress within the quality organization and the company through outstanding personal performance. The person must be well versed, present a good appearance and be capable of meeting and working with all levels of management and personnel, including the vendors and the customers. The person should be capable of supervising calibration technicians, tool and gage personnel and related classifications. The person should be promotable to more responsible positions and willing to increase his/her knowledge through continuous learning via formal education, seminars, and self-education.

GOALS: Promotion to Quality Control—Quality Assurance Supervision and Management positions.

RESPONSIBILITIES:

1. Establish, maintain and supervise calibration system and laboratory.
2. Establish, calibrate, and maintain control of all gages, tools, test equipment, fixtures, working standards and master standards, process control gages, et al.
3. Provide technical assistance to operating departments on calibration or gaging problems.
4. Maintain all calibration and certification records, library and required reference documents.
5. Train and motivate personnel in care and use of tools, gages and measuring-testing devices.
6. Command professional respect of management, personnel, vendors, and the customers.
7. Maintain clean area and environment for efficient and precision work by all personnel.
8. Participate in A.S.Q.C. and/or other Professional and Technical Societies for personal and company growth.
9. Establish budget and controls for purchase of necessary equipment.
10. Evaluate personnel for merit increases and promotions.
11. Communicate—Coordinate—Cooperate with Management and Personnel.

LARGE BUSINESS QUALITY ORGANIZATION

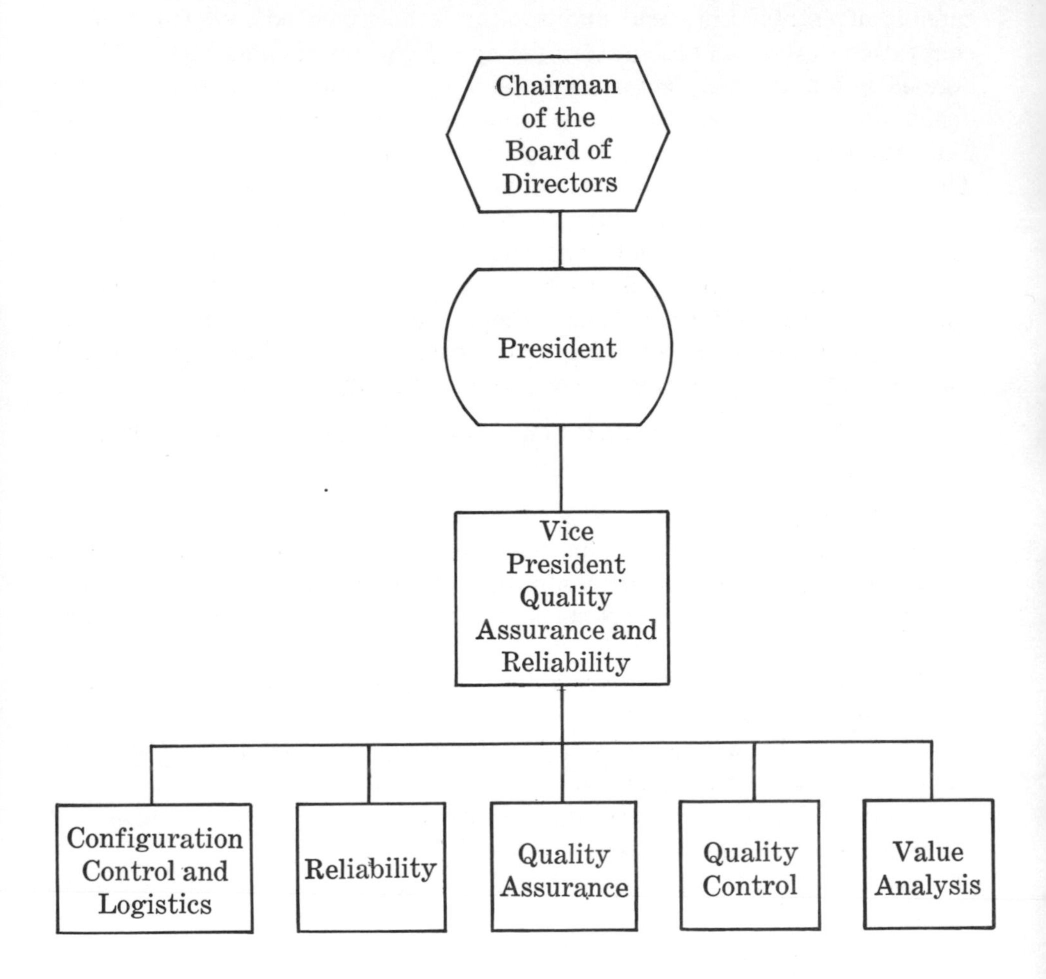

SMALL BUSINESS QUALITY ORGANIZATION

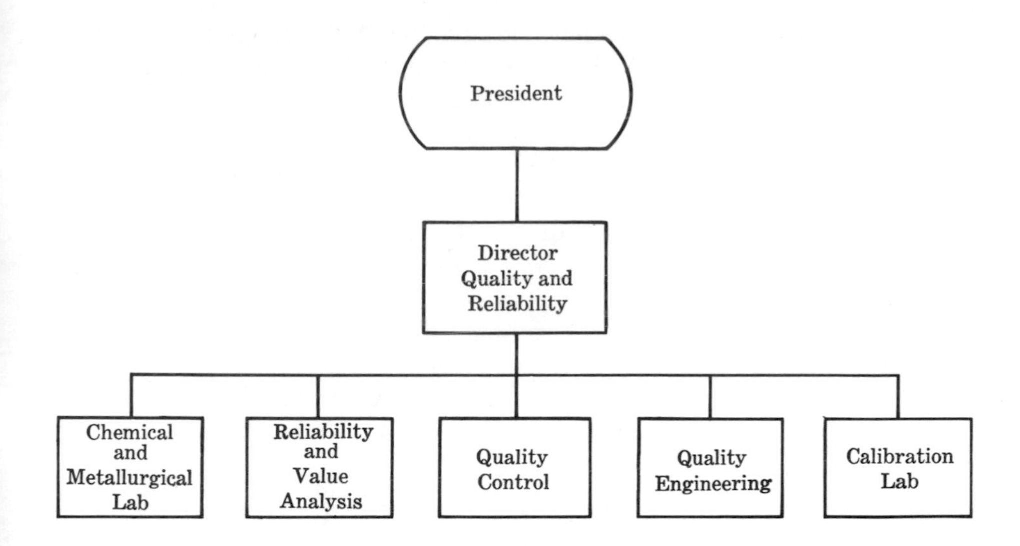

Chapter 5

MANAGEMENT QUALITY ASSURANCE POLICY

Management must create and design the Quality Assurance Policy and Program Plan as related to the structure, products, and services to be furnished by the Company. The management policies can be general in scope, but the actual program plan must be specifically tailored to the method, mode, and operation of the company. Management must assure that the program plan is sound, attainable, and firmly insist on implementation of the Quality Assurance Program Plan for cost-effective "before, during, and after" results.

I have taken the liberty to provide "Typical Management Quality Policy"—from which most all organizations can cost-effectively work to establish an attainable Quality Assurance Program Plan. The resulting Plan can generally be called "The Program for the Control and Assurance of Quality." The following is recommended to be used as a guide:

"TYPICAL MANAGEMENT QUALITY POLICY"

1. **Scope:** This Policy shall apply to **all** organizations within the company. There are no exceptions.

1.1 This policy requires the establishment of a Quality Assurance Program by the company. The Program and Procedures used to implement this Policy shall be developed by the company's Quality Assurance Consultant or the Vice-President of Quality Assurance and Reliability. The Quality Program, including personnel, procedures, processes, and product shall be documented and shall be subject to review and approval by company Executive Management. An effective and economical Quality Program, planned and developed in consonance with the company's other administrative and technical programs, is required by this Policy. Design of the Program shall be based upon consideration of the total structure of the company, technical and manufacturing aspects of production, and related engineering design and materials as appropriate to our operations. The Program shall assure adequate quality throughout all areas. For example: Administration, sales, marketing, design, development, fabrication, processing, assembly, inspection, test, maintenance, packaging, shipping, storage, delivery, installation, and services. Integrity and Customer Satisfaction must be maintained at all levels at all times.

All supplies and services, whether manufactured or performed on company facilities or at any other source, shall be controlled at all points necessary to assure conformance to specific requirements. The Quality Program shall provide for the prevention and ready detection of discrepancies and for timely and positive corrective action. The company shall have objective evidence of quality conformance readily available to those who have the need to know. Instructions and records for quality must be controlled. The Program shall stress Preventive-Before the Fact Quality Assurance.

The authority and responsibility of those in charge of administration, design, production, testing, and inspection of quality shall be clearly stated. The Program shall facilitate early determinations of the effects of quality deficiencies and quality costs on our prices. Facilities and standards such as drawings, engineering changes, measuring equipment and the like which are necessary for the creation of the required quality shall be effectively managed and controlled. The Program shall include an effective control of purchased materials and subcontracted work. Administrative functions, manufacturing, fabrication and assembly work conducted within the company's facilities shall be controlled completely. The Quality Program shall also include effective execution of responsibilities shared jointly with our customers, such as control of customer property and customer source inspection.

The company is responsible for compliance with all provisions of contracts and for furnishing specified supplies and services which meet all the requirements of the contracts. If any inconsistency exists between the contract or its general provisions and this Policy, the contract and the general provisions shall control. The company's Quality Program shall include reliability functions and shall be planned, used and extensively monitored for compliance on a random basis.

2. This Management Policy is effective as of the date shown, and shall not be modified or superseded without controlled re-issuance by Quality Assurance Executive Management.

3. **QUALITY ASSURANCE PROGRAM MANAGEMENT**

3.1 **Organization.** Effective Quality Management shall be clearly prescribed by the company. Personnel performing Quality functions shall have sufficient, well-defined responsibility, authority and the organizational freedom to identify and evaluate quality problems and to initiate, recommend or provide solutions. Executive Management shall regularly review the status and adequacy of the Quality Program. The fulfillment of the requirements of this Policy is the responsibility of all company organizations, functions, and personnel. Quality, Value and Integrity is mandatory.

3.2 **Initial Quality Planning.** The company, during the earliest practical phase of performance, shall conduct a complete review of the requirements of any contract to identify and make timely provision for the administration, special controls, processes, test equipments, fixtures, tooling and skills required for assuring Product Quality. This initial planning will recognize the need and provide for special research, when necessary, to update inspection and testing techniques, instrumentation and correlation of inspection and test results with manufacturing methods and processes. This planning will also provide appropriate review and action to assure compatibility of manufacturing, inspection, testing and documentation. Quality, Value and Integrity is mandatory.

3.3 **Documented Instructions.** The Quality Program shall assure that all work affecting Quality (including such things as purchasing, handling, machining, assembling, fabricating, processing, inspection, testing, modification, installation, and any other treatment of product, facilities, standards or equipment from the ordering of materials to dispatch of shipments) shall be prescribed in clear and complete documented instructions of a type appropriate to the circumstances. The instructions shall provide the criteria for performing the work functions, and shall be compatible with acceptance criteria for workmanship. The instructions are intended also to serve for supervising, inspecting and managing work. The preparation, maintenance of and compliance with documented work instructions shall be monitored as a function of the Quality Program.

3.4 **Records.** The company shall maintain and use any records or data essential to the economical and effective operation of the Quality Program. These records shall be available for review by those who have the need to know. Records are one of the principal forms of objective evidence of Quality. The Quality Program shall assure that records are complete and reliable. Inspection and testing records shall, as a minimum, indicate the nature of the observations together with the number of observations made and the number and type of deficiencies found. Also, records for monitoring work performance and for inspection and testing shall indicate the acceptability of work or products and the corrective action taken in connection with deficiencies. The Quality Assurance Program shall provide for the analysis and use of records as a basis for management action.

3.5 **Corrective Action.** The Quality Assurance Program shall promptly detect and correct assignable conditions adverse to Quality and Reliability. Administration, design, purchasing, manufacturing, testing or other operations which could result in or have resulted in defective supplies, services, facilities, technical data, standards or other elements of performance which could create excessive losses or costs must be identified and changed as a result of the Quality Program. Corrective action will extend to the performance of all suppliers and vendors and will include data and product forwarded from users. Corrective action shall include as a minimum:

(a) Analysis of data and examination of product scrapped or reworked to determine extent and causes;

(b) Analysis of trends in processes or performance of work to prevent nonconforming product; and

(c) Introduction of required improvements and corrections, an initial review of the adequacy of such measures and monitoring of the effectiveness of corrective action taken. Corrective Action is cost effective and mandatory.

3.6 **Costs Related to Quality.** The company shall maintain and use quality cost data as a management element of the Quality Program. These data shall serve the purpose of identifying the cost of both the prevention and correction of nonconforming supplies (e.g., labor and material involved in material spoilage caused by defective work, correction of defective work and for quality control exercised by the company at subcontractor's or vendor's facilities). The specific quality cost data to be maintained and used will be determined by the company. These data shall be reviewed by Executive Management.

4. **DRAWING CONTROL AND CALIBRATION**

4.1 **Drawings, Documentation and Changes.** A procedure shall be maintained that concerns itself with the adequacy, completeness and currentness of drawings and with the control of changes in design. With respect to the currentness of drawings and changes, the company shall assure that requirements for the effectivity point of changes are met, recorded, and that obsolete drawings and change requirements are removed from all points of issue and use.

With respect to design drawings and specifications, a procedure shall be maintained that shall provide for the evaluation of their engineering adequacy and an evaluation of the adequacy of proposed changes. The evaluation shall encompass both the adequacy in relation to standard engineering and design practices and the adequacy with respect to the design and purpose of the product to which the drawing relates.

With respect to supplemental specifications, process instructions, production engineering instructions, industrial engineering instructions and work instructions relating to a particular design, the company shall be responsible for a review of adequacy, currentness and completeness. The Quality Program must provide complete coverage of all information necessary to produce an article in complete conformity with requirements of the design.

The Quality Program shall assure that there is complete compliance with special requirements for proposing, approving, and effecting of engineering changes. The Quality Program shall provide for effectively monitoring compliance with contractual engineering changes requiring approval by the customer.

Delivery of correct drawings and change information to the customer in connection with data acquisition shall be an integral part of the Quality Program. This includes full compliance with contract requirements concerning rights and data, both proprietary and other. The Quality Program's responsibility for drawings and changes extend to the drawings and changes provided by the subcontractors and vendors.

4.2 **Measuring and Testing Equipment.** The company shall provide and maintain gages and other measuring and testing devices necessary to assure that supplies conform to technical requirements. These devices shall be calibrated against certified measurement standards which have known, valid relationships to the National Bureau of Standards at established periods to assure continued accuracy. The objective is to assure that inspection and test equipment is adjusted, replaced or repaired before it becomes inaccurate. The calibration of measuring and testing equipment shall be mandatory. The Quality Assurance Program shall insure the use of only such subcontractor and vendor sources that depend upon calibration systems which effectively control the accuracy of measuring and testing equipment as traceable to the National Bureau of Standards.

4.3 **Production Tooling Used For Inspection.** When production jigs, fixtures, tooling masters, templates, patterns and such other devices are used for inspection, they shall be proved for accuracy prior to release for use. These devices shall be proved again for accuracy at intervals formally established in a manner to cause their timely adjustment, replacement or repair prior to becoming inaccurate.

4.4 **Use of Company Inspection Equipment.** The company gages, measuring and testing devices shall be made available for use by the customer when required to determine conformance with contract requirements within company facilities. If conditions warrant, company personnel shall be made available for operation of such devices and for verification of their accuracy and condition. These customer services shall be subject to management approval.

4.5 **Advanced Metrology Requirements.** The Quality Program shall include timely identification and reports to company Executive Management of any precision measurement needs exceeding the known state of the art.

5. **CONTROL OF PURCHASES**

5.1 **Responsibility.** The company is responsible for assuring that all supplies and services procured from suppliers, subcontractors and vendors conform to the contract requirements. The selection of sources and the nature and extent of control exercised shall be dependent upon the type of supplies, the supplier's demonstrated capability to perform, and the quality evidence made available. To assure an adequate and economical control of such material, the company shall utilize to the fullest extent, objective evidence of quality furnished by our suppliers. The effectiveness and integrity of the control of quality by suppliers shall be assessed and reviewed by the company at intervals consistent with the complexity and quantity of product. Inspection of products upon delivery to the company shall be used for assessment and review to the extent necessary for adequate assurance of quality. Test reports, inspection records, certificates and other suitable evidence relating to the supplier's control of quality should be used in the assessment and review. The responsibility for the control of purchases includes the establishment of a procedure for (1) the selection of qualified suppliers, (2) the transmission of applicable design and quality requirements, (3) the evaluation of the adequacy of procured items, and (4) effective provisions for early information feedback and correction of nonconformances. The company shall use a simple dollar and cents method of rating vendors for clear understanding by company and vendors.

5.2 **Purchasing Data.** The company shall require vendors and subcontractors to have a Quality Program achieving control of the quality of the services and supplies which they provide. The company shall assure that all applicable requirements are properly included or referenced in all purchase orders. The purchase order shall contain a complete description of the supplies ordered, including, by statement or reference, all applicable requirements for manufacturing, inspecting, testing, packaging, and any requirements for inspections, qualification or approvals. Technical requirements of the following nature must be included by statement or reference as a part of the required clear description: all pertinent drawings, engineering change orders, specifications (including inspection system or Quality Program requirements), reliability, safety, weight, or other special requirements, unusual test or inspection procedures or equipment, and any special revision or model identification. The description of products ordered shall include a requirement for company inspection at the vendor's facility when such action is necessary to assure that the vendor's Quality Program effectively implements the responsibility for complete assurance of product quality. Requirements shall be included for chemical and physical testing and recording in connection with the purchase of raw materials by suppliers. The purchase orders must also contain a requirement for suppliers to notify and obtain approval from the company of changes in design of the products. Necessary instructions should be provided when provision is made for direct shipment from the vendor to our customer.

6. **MANUFACTURING CONTROL**

6.1 **Materials and Materials Control.** Supplier's materials and products shall be subjected to inspection upon receipt to the extent necessary to assure conformance to technical requirements. Receiving inspection may be adjusted upon the basis of the Quality Assurance Program exercised by suppliers. Evidence of the supplier's satisfactory control of quality may be used to adjust the amount and kind of receiving inspection.

The Quality Program shall assure that raw materials to be used in fabrication or processing of products conform to the applicable physical, chemical, and other technical requirements. Laboratory testing shall be employed as necessary. Suppliers shall be required by the Quality Program to exercise equivalent control of the raw materials utilized in the production of the parts and items which they supply to our company. Raw material awaiting testing must be separately identified or segregated from already tested and approved material, but can be released for initial production, providing that identification and control is maintained. Material tested and approved must be kept identified until such time as its identity is necessarily obliterated by processing. Strict controls will be established to prevent the inadvertent use of material failing to pass tests.

6.2 **Production Processing and Fabrication.** The company Quality Program must assure that all machining, wiring, batching, shaping and all basic production operations of any type, together with all processing and fabricating of any type, is accomplished under controlled conditions. Controlled conditions include documented work instructions, adequate production equipment, and any special working environment. Documented work instructions are considered to be the criteria for much of the production, processing and fabrication work. These instructions are the criteria for acceptable or unacceptable "workmanship." The Quality Program will effectively monitor the issuance of and compliance with all of these work instructions. A company Quality Assurance Workmanship Standards Manual is mandatory.

Physical examination, measurement or tests of the material or products processed is necessary for each work operation and must also be conducted under controlled conditions. If physical inspection of processed material is impossible or disadvantageous, indirect control by monitoring processing methods, equipment and personnel shall be provided. Both physical inspection and process monitoring shall be provided when control is inadequate without both.

Inspection and monitoring of processed material or products shall be accomplished in any suitable systematic manner selected by the company. Methods of inspection and monitoring shall be corrected any time their unsuitability with reasonable evidence is demonstrated. Adherence to selected methods for inspection and monitoring shall be complete and continuous. Corrective measures shall be taken when noncompliance occurs.

Inspection by machine operators, automated inspection gages, moving line or lot sampling, setup or first piece approval, production line inspection station, inspection or test department, roving inspectors or any other type of inspection, shall be employed in any combination desired by the company which will adequately and efficiently protect product quality and the integrity of processing. Criteria for approval and rejection shall be provided for all inspection of product and monitoring of methods, equipment, and personnel. Means for identifying approved and rejected product shall be provided.

Certain chemical, metallurgical, biological, sonic, electronic, and radiological processes are of so complex and specialized a nature that much more than the ordinary detailing of work documentation is required. In effect, such processing may require an entire work specification as contrasted with the normal work operation instructions established in normal plant-wide standard production control issuances such as job operation routing tags and the like. For these special processes, the Quality Program shall assure that the process control procedure or specifications are adequate and that processing environments and the certifying, inspection, authorization and monitoring of such processes to the special degree necessary for these ultra-precise and super-complex work functions are provided.

6.3 **Inspection and Testing.** The Quality Program shall assure that there is a system for final inspection and testing of completed products. Such testing shall provide a measure of the overall quality of the completed product and shall be performed so that it simulates, to a sufficient degree, product end use and functioning. Such simulation frequently involves appropriate life and endurance tests and qualification testing. Final inspection and testing shall provide for reporting to designers any unusual difficulties, deficiencies or questionable conditions. When modifications, repairs or replacements are required after final inspection or testing, there shall be reinspection and retesting of any characteristics affected.

6.4 **Handling, Storage and Delivery.** The Quality Program shall provide for adequate work and inspection instructions for handling, storage, preservation, packaging, and shipping to protect the quality of products and prevent damage, loss, deterioration, degradation, or substitution of products. With respect to handling, the Quality Program shall require and monitor the use of procedures to prevent 'handling damage' to articles. Handling procedures of this type include the use of special crates, boxes, containers, transportation vehicles and any other facilities for materials handling. Means shall be provided for any necessary protection against deterioration or damage to products in storage. Periodic inspection for the prevention and results of such deterioration or damage shall be provided. Products subject to deterioration or corrosion during fabrication or interim storage shall be cleaned and preserved by methods which will protect against such deterioration or corrosion. When necessary, package designing and packaging shall include means for accommodating and maintaining critical environments within packages, e.g., moisture content levels, gas pressures. The Quality Program shall assure that when such packaging environments must be maintained, packages are labeled to indicate this condition. The Quality Program shall monitor shipping work to assure that products shipped are accompanied with required shipping and technical documents, and that compliance with Interstate Commerce Commission rules and other applicable shipping regulations is effected to assure safe arrival and identification at destination. In compliance with contractual requirements, the Quality Program shall include monitoring provisions for protection of the quality of products during transit.

6.5 **Nonconforming Material.** The company shall establish and maintain an effective and positive system for controlling nonconforming material, including procedures for its identification, segregation, and disposition. Repair or rework of nonconforming materal shall be in accordance with documented procedures. All nonconforming supplies shall be positively identified to prevent unauthorized use, shipment and intermingling with conforming supplies. Holding areas and specific procedures shall be provided.

6.6 **Statistical Quality Control and Analysis.** In addition to statistical methods, statistical planning, analysis, tests and quality control, other techniques may be utilized whenever they are suitable to maintain the required control of quality. Sampling plans may be used when tests are destructive, or when the records, inherent characteristics of the product or the noncritical application of the product, indicate that a reduction in inspection or testing can be achieved without jeopardizing quality. The company may employ sampling inspection in accordance with applicable military standards and sampling plans (e.g., from MIL-STD-105, MIL-STD-414, or Handbooks H 106, 107 and 108). Any sampling plan used shall provide valid confidence and quality levels.

6.7 **Indication of Inspection Status.** The company shall maintain a positive system for identifying the inspection status of products. Identification may be accomplished by means of signature, stamps, tags, routing cards, move tickets, tote box cards or other normal control devices.

NOTE: Paragraph 7 applies to government contracts only.

7. **COORDINATED GOVERNMENT/CONTRACTOR ACTIONS**

7.1 **Government Inspection at Subcontractor or Vendor Facilities.** The Government reserves the right to inspect at source, supplies or services not manufactured or performed at the company's facility. Government inspection shall not constitute acceptance; nor shall it in any way replace company inspection or otherwise relieve the company of our responsibility to furnish an acceptable end item. The purpose of this inspection is to assist the Government Representative at the company's facility to determine the conformance of supplies or services with contract requirements. Such inspection can only be requested by or under authorization of the Government Representative. When Government inspection is required, the company shall add to our purchasing document the following statement:

> "Government inspection is required prior to shipment from your plant. Upon receipt of this order, promptly notify the Government Representative who normally services your plant so that appropriate planning for Govern-

ment inspection can be accomplished."

When, under authorization of the Government Representative, copies of the purchasing document are to be furnished directly by the subcontractor or vendor to the Government Representative at his facility rather than through Government channels, the company shall add to our purchasing document a statement substantially as follows:

"On receipt of this order, promptly furnish a copy to the Government Representative who normally services your plant, or, if none, to the nearest Army, Navy, Air Force, or Defense Supply Agency inspection office. In the event the representative or office cannot be located, our purchasing agent should be notified immediately."

All documents and referenced data for purchases applying to a Government contract shall be available for review by the Government Representative to determine compliance with the requirements for the control of such purchases. Copies of purchasing documents required for Government purposes shall be furnished in accordance with the instructions of the Government Representative. The company shall make available to the Government Representative reports of any nonconformance found on Government source inspected supplies and shall (when requested) require the supplier to coordinate with his Government Representative on corrective action.

7.2 Government Property.

7.2.1 Government-furnished Material. When material is furnished by the Government, our company's procedures shall include at least the following:

(a) Examination upon receipt, consistent with practicability to detect damage in transit;

(b) Inspection for completeness and proper type;

(c) Periodic inspection and precautions to assure adequate storage conditions and to guard against damage from handling and deterioration during storage;

(d) Functional testing, either prior to or after installation, or both, as required by contract to determine satisfactory operation;

(e) Identification and protection from improper use or disposition; and,

(f) Verification of quality.

7.2.2 Damaged Government-furnished Material. The company shall report to the Government Representative any Government-furnished material found damaged, malfunctioning, or otherwise unsuitable for use. In the event of damage or malfunctioning during or after installation, the company shall determine and record probable cause and necessity for withholding material from use.

7.2.3 **Bailed Property.** The company shall, as required by the terms of the Bailment Agreement, establish procedures for the adequate storage, maintenance, and inspection of bailed Government property. Records of all inspections and maintenance performed on bailed property shall be maintained. These procedures and records shall be subject to review by the Government Representative.

8. **Customer Services.** The Company shall cooperate with the customer and make every effort to achieve customer satisfaction through Communication, Coordination, and Cooperation, Quality, Value, and Integrity.

In addition to the "Typical Management Quality Policy" as provided, I want to furnish the very latest information to you as generated by the "National Vendor-Vendee Technical Committee" of the American Society for Quality Control. As a past-chairman and active member of this committee, I can attest to the many, many committee and subcommittee meetings as held over a period of several years to generate and coordinate this "Specification of General Requirements for a Quality Program" as a proposed unified American Society for Quality Control Standard to be used on a universal basis. I believe this ASQC STD-C1, as proposed, is good sound Quality management at its best. The following chapter covers the general requirements for a Quality Program.

Chapter 6

UNIVERSAL QUALITY PROGRAM REQUIREMENTS

For many years, small, medium, and large business and industry has been faced with the problem of creating, adjusting, and modifying quality programs in order to meet contractual requirements which have varied from customer to customer, which have often been in conflict, and which have frequently usurped management prerogatives to the point of preventing the operation of an effective and economical quality program.

Recognizing a need for a specification which could be universally applied to the manufacture or procurement of any products or services, including commercial, industrial, or governmental, and which could be applied to organizations of any size, this Standard was prepared.

The underlying philosophy of this Quality Program Standard is to provide uniform guiding principles that may be used as the basis for planning, operating, and evaluating a quality program, either within an organization or as a contractual understanding between buyer and seller.

The basic concepts involved are:

(1) The general nature and intent of a Quality Program should be expressed in statements of objectives that meet the needs of producers, customers, and users of the concerned products and services.

(2) The philosophies and objectives of a Quality Program should be extended to procedures and instructions that are workable and verifiable in practical operating circumstances, and

(3) The Quality Program should be judged in terms of the extent to which it is actually and economically accomplishing the intent of the program objectives.

The Quality Assurance Program must be tailored to the individual company. This will result in a cost effective program for the control and assurance of quality, reliability, maintainability, value, safety, service, and integrity. The Quality Assurance Program must encompass the entire operation of the company, from initial design engineering through purchasing, manufacturing, quality, marketing, sales, and delivery to the satisfied customers. Every person in the company must be on the management and personnel team for attainment of quality, value, and integrity. There should be no exceptions. Compliance to the Quality Program should be mandatory. Every person must understand the

Quality Program, and this can only be accomplished by complete training, motivation, and education of all levels of management and personnel. Then, and only then, will the Quality Program be a cost effective success for the company.

The Quality Assurance Program should extend into the administrative and general office functions of every company. The quality of the work of the secretary or clerk typist is just as important as that of the milling machine operator. The letter she types must be perfect. That letter could result in new business. That letter, with mistakes, could cost you many customers and lots of money. The clerk must file orders correctly. If not filed properly, customers will be dissatisfied when their orders are not completed on schedule. Yes, Quality Control in the office is a very important part of the Quality Program. However, most companies do not associate quality control with administrative and general office functions. Yes, I am very serious. Have you taken time to inspect your letters? Please do. The results will be shocking. Cut the cost of quality by reducing typing errors. You can accomplish many things by utilizing the new Universal Quality Program Standard.

This Standard recommends general principles relating to the requirements for quality programs and is one of a series of ASQC Standards. It contains information secured from many sources, notably from the National Vendor-Vendee Technical Committee of ASQC. Many years of dedicated work by professional quality engineers and managers have gone into the preparation of this management document. Suggestions for improvement based on the actual use of this Standard will be welcome. They should be sent to the American Society for Quality Control, 161 West Wisconsin Avenue, Milwaukee, Wisconsin 53203. Attention: Vendor-Vendee Technical Committee.

The Vendor-Vendee Technical Committee, which proposed this Standard, was composed of the following persons:

A. F. Cone	Sandia Corporation
Lawrence Swaton	Martin Company
David L. Field	Sandia Corporation
C. L. Carter, Jr.	C. L. Carter, Jr. and Asso., Inc.
Jack B. Foster	North American Aviation
M. M. Minardi	Autonetics
W. H. Anderson	General Electric Company
Howard N. Wilson	Bendix Corporation
Ray Vandersanden	Tektronix, Inc.

Thomas L. Bair	Texas Instruments, Inc.
Olin K. Crouch	R. J. Reynolds Tobacco Co.
Richard K. Smith	North American Van Lines
E. W. Ellis	Pratt & Whitney Aircraft
A. L. Wilson	Hewlett-Packard Associates

We regret that our Past-Chairman, A. F. Cone, passed away before the C-1 Standard was formally approved. His dedicated work on the Vendor-Vendee Committee will not be forgotten.

GENERAL REQUIREMENTS FOR A QUALITY PROGRAM
ASQC Std. C-1

1. Definition of Terms

1.1 **Quality Program**—The system of activities established to provide a quality of product or service that meets the needs of users.

1.2 **Contractor**—A term used herein to designate the individual or organization on whom this Standard is imposed.

1.3 **Buyer**—A term used herein to designate the individual or organization that imposes this Standard on a contractor.

NOTE: When this Standard is used internally, the contractor may be a single shop or production group and the buyer may be a management or staff group empowered to specify the use of this Standard.

1.4 **Inspection**—The process of measuring, examining, testing, gaging, or otherwise comparing one or more units of product with the applicable requirements.

2. Scope

2.1 **Applicability**—When this Standard is prescribed or specified by contract or agreement, it provides a specification of the general requirements to be met by the quality program of a contractor or other organization. All the requirements apply to a given contract except to the extent that they are specifically deleted, supplemented, or amended in the contract.

2.2 **General Purpose**—This Standard requires the establishment and maintenance of a quality program by the contractor and his subcontractors to assure compliance with the requirements of the contract. The quality program, including its procedures and operations, shall be documented by the contractor and shall be subject to review of the buyer's representative.

The program shall apply to the control of quality throughout all areas of contract performance including, as appropriate, the procurement, identification, stocking, and issue of material; the entire process of manufacture; and the packaging, storing, and shipping of material.

The program shall provide that, as early as possible, discrepancies (defects and program deficiencies) shall be discovered and corrective action taken.

3. **Requirements**

3.1 **Quality Management**

3.1.1 **General**—There shall be adequate planning, forceful direction, and control in the sense of measurement and evaluation of the effectiveness of the quality program.

3.1.2 **Organization**—Administration of the quality program shall be vested in a responsible, authoritative element of the organization, with a clear access to management. This organization shall be staffed by technically competent personnel with freedom to make decisions without hint of pressure or bias. It shall also have sufficient authority to ensure that quality requirements are consistently maintained.

3.1.3 **Procedures**—Written quality control, test, and inspection procedures shall be used for all pertinent operations. These procedures shall be kept current and shall be available at all locations where they will be used.

3.2 **Design Information**

3.2.1 **General**—Design information for a product (such as drawings, specifications, and standards) shall be maintained to ensure that items are fabricated, inspected, and tested to the latest applicable requirements. In like manner, task definitions for a service shall be maintained to ensure that the services are performed and inspected to the latest applicable requirements.

3.2.2 **Change Control**—All changes to design information or task definition shall be processed in a manner that will ensure accomplishment as specified, and a record of actual incorporation points (by date, batch, lot, unit, or other specific identification) shall be maintained.

3.3 **Procurement**

3.3.1 **General**—Adequate control over procurement sources shall be maintained to ensure that services and supplies conform to specified requirements, including this specification. Purchase orders (or contracts) shall be controlled to ensure incorporation of pertinent technical and quality requirements, including authorized changes. Adequate records of inspections and tests performed on purchased material shall be maintained.

3.3.2 **Source Inspection**—The buyer and his authorized representatives reserve the right to inspect, at the source, any supplies furnished or services rendered under this contract. Inspection at the source shall not necessarily constitute acceptance, nor shall it relieve the seller of his responsibility to furnish acceptable product. When it is not practical or feasible to determine quality conformance of purchased items, inspection at the source is authorized.

3.3.3 **Fabricated Material**—All purchased material shall be evaluated to assure conformance with the requirements of applicable standards and specifications. When required, shipment of materials shall be accompanied by certified test reports that demonstrate the conformance of raw material, plating, etc., to the requirements stated in the purchase order or product specification. When submission of certified test reports is not specifically required, every shipment shall be accompanied by a certificate stating that conformance to all requirements has been ascertained, that quantitative data reports are on file, and that copies of test results will be furnished on request. The validity of certifications shall be verified periodically. Provisions will be made for withholding from use all incoming supplies pending completion of each required inspection and test or receipt of necessary test reports. The seller shall be notified whenever nonconforming materials are received, and corrective action shall be initiated when warranted.

3.3.4 **Raw Materials**—Raw material shall normally be tested to determine conformance to applicable specifications. Unless otherwise required by the purchase order or the product specification, certified test reports identifiable with the material may be accepted in lieu of such tests. When certifications are used as a basis for acceptance, the test results shall be compared with specification requirements. Furthermore, the validity of certifications shall be periodically verified by independent testing.

3.4 **Material Control**—Adequate methods and facilities shall be established for controlling the identification, handling, and storage of raw and fabricated material. The identification shall include indications of the inspection status of the material. These controls shall be maintained from the time of receipt of the material until delivery to the customer, in order to protect the material from damage, deterioration, loss, or substitution.

3.5 **Manufacture**

3.5.1 **General**—Sufficient control shall be maintained over manufacturing processes to prevent excessive product defectiveness and variability, and to assure conformance of the characteristics of product, which can be verified only at the time and point of manufacture.

3.5.2 **Process Control**—Evaluations and controls shall be established and maintained at appropriately located points in the manufacturing process to assure continuous control of quality of parts, components, and assemblies.

3.5.3 **Special Processes**—Adequate methods and facilities shall be provided to assure conformance with requirements for special process specifications, such as welding, plating, anodizing, nondestructive testing, heat-treating, soldering, and testing of materials. Certifications, such as those for personnel, procedures, and equipment, shall be maintained as required.

3.6 **Acceptance**

3.6.1 **General**—Inspection and testing of completed material shall be performed as necessary to assure that contract requirements have been met. Sufficient surveillance shall be maintained over preservation, marking, packing, and shipping operations to assure compliance with requirements and to prevent damage, deterioration, loss, or substitutions.

3.6.2 **Sampling Inspection**—Any acceptance sampling procedures that differ from those required by the contract shall afford adequate assurance that the quality meets acceptable levels, and shall be approved by the buyer.

3.6.3 **Nonconforming Material**—Procedures and facilities for the handling of nonconforming material shall require prominent identification of the material and prompt removal from the work area. Unless otherwise provided in the product specification, the seller may, at his option, scrap the material or request disposition instructions from the buyer.

3.7 **Measuring Instruments**—Accuracy of measurements and tests shall be assured through the use of suitable inspection measuring and test equipment of the range, accuracy, and type necessary to determine conformance of articles to contract requirements. At intervals established to ensure continued accuracy, measuring devices shall be verified or calibrated against certified standards that have a known, valid relationship to national standards. Tooling used as media of inspection shall be included in this program. Furthermore, every device so verified shall bear an indication attesting to the current status and showing the date (or other basis) on which inspection or recalibration is next required.

3.8 **Quality Information**

3.8.1 **General**—Information from control areas described in Paragraphs 3.1 through 3.7 of this specification shall be systematically utilized for the prevention, detection, and correction of deficiencies in the program that affect quality.

3.8.2 **Quality Control Records**—For all inspections and tests, records that include data on both conforming and nonconforming products shall be maintained. A continuing review of these records shall be made and summary information shall be reported periodically to responsible management.

3.8.3. **Corrective Action**—Prompt action shall be taken to correct conditions that cause defective materials. Use shall be made of feedback data generated by the customer as well as data generated internally.

4. **Quality Program Audits**

Quality programs will be audited by the buyer for conformance to the intent of this specification. Disapproval of the program or major portions thereof may be cause for withholding acceptance of product.

UNIVERSAL-INTERNATIONAL USE

The quality program must be a management program. The quality program must be "personnel oriented" for complete understanding and everyday use. The quality program is an outstanding sales and marketing tool. It is—and should be—used to the greatest benefit of the company to increase profit and customer satisfaction. This can only be accomplished when the program is installed, implemented, and functioning in every respect.

The quality program will provide confidence to your customers. The quality program will be subject to **professional** survey, audit, and surveillance by your customers or their designated representatives. Your management should welcome the opportunity to display the company's capabilities and should extend the invitation to customers and prospective customers to conduct a professional review of the quality program by visiting the facilities, consistent with proper notification and appointment. Please note that I stress **professional** survey, audit, and surveillance and **professional** review of the quality program.

The ASQC Standard C-1 is good sound quality management at its best. I trust it will be accepted for use as the Universal Quality Program Specification and be adopted as the **international standard** of "General Requirements for a Quality Program". This Standard applies to any and all business, industry, or government agency. Use it in your company for cost-effective results.

Chapter 7

THE QUALITY ASSURANCE PROGRAM

Based on the Total Quality Assurance concept of operation, I am providing a portion of an actual Quality Assurance Program and Procedures Manual, prepared and installed within one of my client companies. This is provided for information and guidance purposes, and is not to be construed as being the specific Program which should be used in your company. As I have stated, **the Quality Assurance Program must be tailored to your company's specific needs.**

Please note that the Quality Assurance Procedures Manual has been fully approved by all Executive Levels of Management, with concurrence of the cognizant Government Agency.

The Total Quality Assurance Procedures Manual will basically fulfill the requirements of the Management Quality Assurance Policy and the American Society for Quality Control Standard C-1, as previously covered.

It was prepared to meet or exceed the requirements as might be invoked by any customer as appropriate to the size of that firm and the products and services rendered.

The Total Quality Assurance Procedures Manual, of which a portion is described, is in operation and achieving cost-effective results for the company and its customers.

NELSON ELECTRONICS LABORATORIES, INC. • DALLAS NORTH RESEARCH PARK
1717 DALLAS NORTH PARKWAY • PLANO, TEXAS

NELSON ELECTRONICS LABORATORIES, INC.
QUALITY ASSURANCE PROCEDURES
MANUAL

NO. 2

Q.A. PROCEDURES MANUAL

TABLE OF CONTENTS

INTRODUCTION

Our company specializes in the repair, modification, maintenance, calibration, and related sales associated with a wide range of precision meters and electrical test equipment. We are privileged to be approved representatives for the country's leading manufacturers of this type of equipment and are sanctioned as their qualified and certified agency for any work to be done on their equipment.

We also specialize in the calibration, maintenance and repair of precision electrical test equipment and the calibration of working and secondary standards for commercial, military, space and scientific oriented firms and educational institutions. All calibration is directly traceable to the National Bureau of Standards via our primary standards. Our calibration system conforms to Mil-C-45662.

Our efforts in both of the above specialized areas has qualified our organization for producing quality electrical and electronic assemblies to exacting quality and precise workmanship standards. We are prepared to quote to your specifications.

Our customers and prospective customers are invited to review our facilities for quality assurance and assembly manufacturing or related assignments in our areas of specialization by pre-arranging anticipated surveys with members of our management staff.

PURPOSE AND INTENT

Our quality assurance program has been prepared by management to assure the quality, reliability, value and integrity of the products and services we deliver or provide to our customers. The total program for cost effective control is based upon the sound practical approach of providing products and services of acceptable quality at the lowest cost, on time.

The functioning quality assurance procedures contained herein, meet or exceed customer requirements and have been designed to comply with the intent of the following referenced documents of the latest issue: MIL-Q-9858; MIL-I-45208; NASA NPC 200-3; MIL-C-45662; FAA Requirements and ASQC Standard-C1 Quality Program Requirements.

All personnel are responsible for doing their assignments and daily tasks right, the first time thus instilling an atmosphere conducive to high levels of quality and reliability. Compliance with the stated policies and procedures is compulsory.

Revisions to the program for control are under the jurisdiction of the quality assurance department to assure compatability of manufacture, repair, inspection, test, and calibration as appropriate to the specific job. All quality assurance procedures manuals are controlled by serial numbers and assigned to individuals who are responsible for their copy and for immediate compliance to revisions as published by quality assurance.

APPROVAL AND ACCEPTANCE

This Quality Assurance Procedures Manual is hereby approved and accepted for use by all personnel as of the date shown.

R. E. Erickson,
Chief Executive Officer

C. D. Shilling, Vice Pres.
Operations Manager, Plano

Ray Gann, Vice President
Operations Manager, Houston

C. L. Carter, Jr., Director,
Quality Assurance,
Management Consultant

February, 1966

DCASR Concurrance

NELSON ELECTRONICS LABORATORIES, INC.

ORGANIZATION CHART

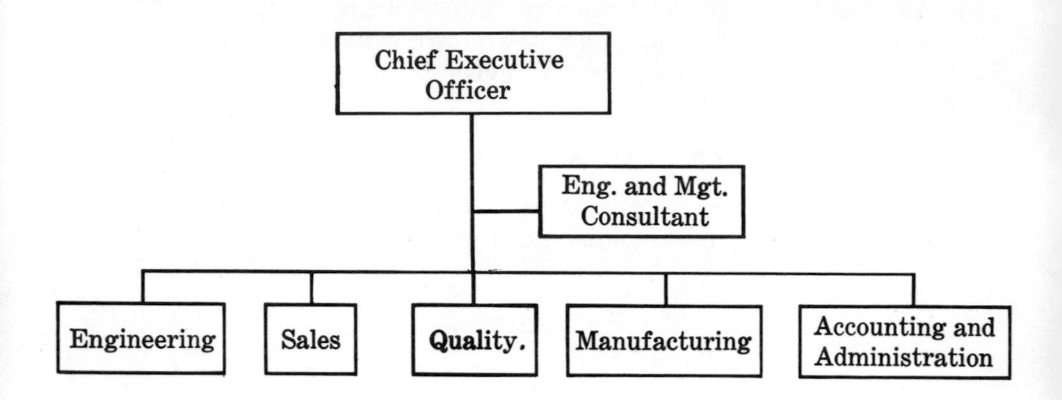

ORGANIZATION FOR QUALITY

The Quality Assurance Director is responsible for administering the total Quality Program. He reports directly to the President and is vested with the authority required to assure customer satisfaction and to maintain and promote our company as a leader in the field of Quality.

The Chief Inspector administers the day-to-day functions of the Quality Control System and is delegated his authority by the Director of Quality Assurance to whom he reports.

The Quality Organization consists of three (3) basic departments as shown below in detail.

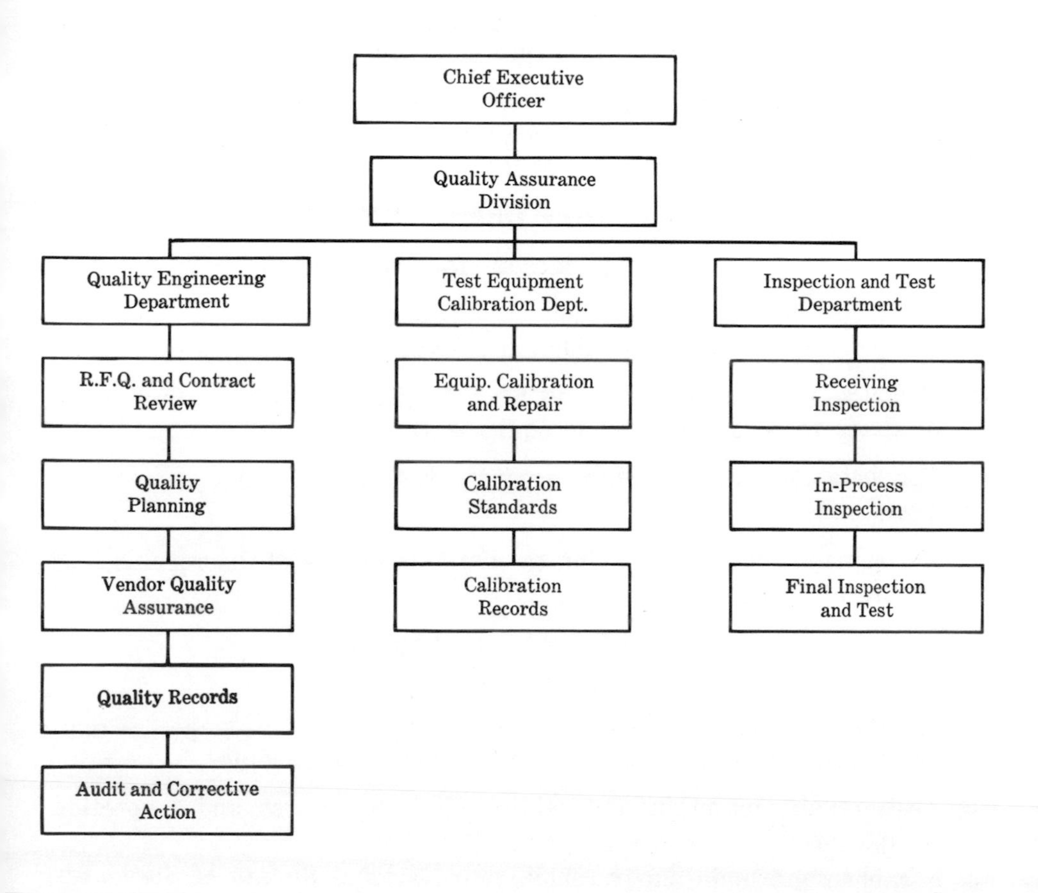

QUALITY ENGINEERING DEPARTMENT

The Quality Engineering Department provides the following functions:

1. Reviews requests for quotes and resulting contracts. Prepares, coordinates and issues Quality Plans and Procedures to insure compliance with contractual obligations, company policies and workmanship standards. Obtain customer concurrence of Quality Plan when directed by contract.

2. Reviews Purchase Orders for Quality conformance and conduct vendor surveys as necessary.

3. Maintain files of all appropriate Quality Records and associated information. Issue and maintain records of all inspection/test stamps.

4. Conduct Quality Audits, issue reports and follow up for corrective action. Provide Quality Assurance representative on Material Review Board and maintain associated M.R.B. records.

INSPECTION DEPARTMENT

The Inspection Department provides the following functions:

1. Conducts Receiving Inspection on items/materials and/or customer equipments used in the production of products for sale to customers.

2. Conducts regular inprocess and Final Inspection/Tests on Production products, meters and customer equipment.

3. Conducts Packing and Shipping Inspection on all items prior to delivery.

4. Recommends corrective action to eliminate causes of discrepancies or failures.

TEST EQUIPMENT CALIBRATION DEPARTMENT

1. Maintain and calibrate company inspection/test tools, gages, instruments and appropriate standards per established schedules.

2. Test, repair, maintain and calibrate customer test and inspection equipment.

3. Establish and maintain traceability to National Bureau of Standards

per stated schedules.

4. Identify all inspection/test equipment and standards and maintain associated records for control.

PLANNING AND INSTRUCTIONS

The Marketing, Engineering and Quality Assurance Division personnel review RFQ's, contracts and/or drawings in order to effectively bid and/or plan for each job. This is accomplished to assure that all contract requirements will be met and that all necessary production and inspection methods and equipment are or will be available as needed to satisfactorily produce the job on time and at the lowest cost. A pre-release and/or design review meeting is held on all released production jobs by the responsible engineering, quality and manufacturing personnel. All cognizant personnel collaborate in the performance of any special instructions, inspections, processes, or tests which must be performed to insure acceptable quality, proper pricing and a prompt production and delivery schedule.

Written manufacturing, inspection and test instructions are prepared and issued to the respective producing departments for manufacture and control of each operation on each job. Drawings and specifications are used to the fullest extent possible to reduce unnecessary paperwork and to supplement written instructions.

Quality Engineering prepares and maintains "Inspection Check Lists" for the various types of items produced and monitors for compliance on a random basis. Process standards and procedures are provided for all special processes used by the company.

Workmanship standards are prepared and documented by Quality Engineering. The "Workmanship Standards Manual" is adhered to unless otherwise directed or stipulated by the Customer. The manual is under the control of the Quality Assurance Division with changes, additions or deletions made to maintain acceptable quality and compatibility with the latest techniques.

CORRECTIVE ACTION

This procedure establishes a formal method for obtaining corrective action at any phase, when normal daily operating procedures do not produce satisfactory results.

A "Request for Corrective Action" form is initiated by either the Quality, Engineering, Manufacturing or Marketing Division as appropriate at any time satisfactory corrective action cannot be obtained by normal day to day operating procedures. The request is forwarded to the Chief Inspector who will immediately investigate reported conditions and recommend to management the action necessary to correct problem areas. Immediate action will be taken by responsible departments to correct any known or reported conditions which may adversely affect the quality of our products.

Documented corrective action forms are initiated on all vendor and customer originated problems. The Chief Inspector will formally reply to all requests for corrective action received from customers pertaining to quality problems. A "Customer Returned Material Record" is maintained and reviewed to allow for prompt corrective action as appropriate.

Corrective Action encompasses all phases and departments concerned with the operation of the company from design through shipping and extends to our vendors, sub-contractors and customers. The Quality Assurance Division investigates recurring discrepancies and provides follow up on corrective action for cost effective control.

RECORDS

The use of adequate records is a major factor of an effective and objective Quality Assurance Program. Records are initiated, maintained and utilized from the R.F.Q. and contract phase, through design, purchasing, manufacturing, inspection, test, and shipping phases.

Typical records are shown in the "Exhibits Section" of this manual and are generally explained in the appropriate paragraphs concerning their intended function and use.

Management reviews all appropriate records, including costs related to quality (i.e. Vendor quality, scrap, rework, corrective action, etc.) on a regular basis for management decisions and action concerning necessary changes, preventive or corrective action.

Records are normally retained for three (3) years unless otherwise stipulated by contract. Appropriate records are available for review when approved by our management, for those who have the need to know and can furnish proper justification.

DRAWING—SPECIFICATION AND CHANGE CONTROL

All items are manufactured, inspected and/or tested to the latest applicable drawing or specification. The following procedure provides a systematic method for the initiation, release, reproduction and distribution of drawings, specifications, instructions and any appropriate changes thereto.

It is the responsibility of the Engineering/Planning Department to:

1. Initiate and provide clear detailed drawings, specifications and/or instructions which conform to customer requirements to all appropriate operating departments of the company for their intended use in purchasing, manufacturing and related quality assurance functions.
2. Control company drawings and specifications by number, date and revision code.
3. Control and maintain file of customer furnished drawings/specifications/sketches for reference and use.
4. Control distribution by job number and producing department as recorded on Job History Record.
5. Control changes by code revision numbers on Job History Record.
6. Issue only latest applicable copies of drawings/specifications. Retrieve and destroy obsolete copies from operating departments when changes are made during the manufacturing cycle of an order.

   NOTE: Should it be necessary to make immediate changes on company drawings or instructions during manufacturing, the change must be made in RED and be signed and dated by the Project Engineer on **each** affected drawing in **all** operating departments. **Every** drawing must be changed as stated for effective coordination and communication. NOTE: **The above shall only be done in emergencies.**
7. Supply Purchasing with copies of controlled drawings for their Vendors.
8. Advise Sales and jointly notify customers of:
   - 8.1 Changes made to Company products which might adversely affect form, fit, function or safety.
   - 8.2 Problems encountered with customer drawings, etc.
9. Maintain an active file of required military and reference documents for company use.

It is the responsibility of each authorized department and individual to:

1. Maintain control of drawings/specifications in their possession at

all times. Return drawings/specifications to Engineering/Planning Department upon completion of job or when the print is no longer needed.

2. Immediately report any problems with drawings to your supervisor for corrective action with Engineering/Planning Department.
3. Refrain from defacing or destroying the drawing, specification or instruction and treat each as one of the company's prime documents.

The Quality Assurance Division will audit the drawing control operation and the files on all active drawings/specifications and related documents for conformance to the stated procedures on a random basis at least once a month and obtain corrective action when necessary.

INSPECTION AND TEST EQUIPMENT

The Test Equipment Calibration Department is responsible for all inspection and test equipment and for maintaining our calibration system in accordance with MIL-C-45662.

Any calibration agencies or vendors used by our company must have calibration systems acceptable to our Quality Assurance Division.

All standards used for calibrating inspection, test equipment or customer standards are traceable to the National Bureau of Standards. The established periods for calibration are based on the particular piece of equipment, its known stability, purpose and degree of usage. Intervals will be changed as records indicate the need. All active inspection/test equipment and standards shall be identified with the following as typical: "Date of Calibration; Calibrated by; Due Date for next Calibration."

Any inspection/test equipment or standards not in use is identified and stored or as applicable may be identified as "Not to be used for Acceptance" or "For indicating purposes only."

"TYPICAL INTERVALS OF CALIBRATION"

	Maximum
Test Equipment used for Acceptance of Product and/or Calibration (Scopes, Bridge, Voltmeters)	6 months
Standards, Primary	12 months
Standards, Secondary	6 months
Gage Blocks	
working	6 months
master	12 months
Micrometers, Calipers, etc.	3 months

Q.A. Procedures Manual

Wire Strippers, mechanical	1 month
Wire Strippers, automatic	Each set up, hourly and random piece audit

The use of company inspection/test equipment will be made available for use by the customer per contract requirements and/or when approved by our management.

VENDOR QUALITY ASSURANCE

Adequate control over procurement sources is mandatory. Our specification "Quality Assurance Requirements for Vendors" Q.A.P. 101 is invoked at the discretion of the Quality Engineering Department depending on the nature and types of items being purchased. Approved vendors are obtained from our company approved source list and/or customer dictated sources. Based on the above, close control is maintained over purchase orders to assure the procurement of quality parts and materials. Purchase orders are reviewed for the following details:

1. Part and/or Drawing Numbers; Nomenclature/Specifications
2. Special Process Information
3. Test/Certification Data Requirements
4. Inspection/Quality Requirements (Company Source Inspection Q.A.P. 101, G.S.I.)
5. Approved Source/Vendor
6. Contract/Job number
7. Pack and Ship Instructions

Records are maintained of all drawings furnished to outside Vendors. The vendors are instructed to return drawings upon completion of orders. When engineering change orders affect vendors, purchasing informs the vendor via a purchase order change notice with an attached copy of the revised drawing.

All purchased items shall be inspected at source or upon receipt in accordance with the Receiving/Receiving Inspection section of this manual.

When G.S.I. is required by the Government on materials to be purchased, the following statement shall be added to the P. O.

> "Government inspection is required prior to shipment from your plant. Upon receipt of this order, promptly notify the government representative who normally services your plant so that appropriate planning for government inspection can be

accomplished."

Should N.E.L. source inspection be necessary, due to critical internal characteristics of the items or the item requires complex testing only available at the vendors, the following statement shall be added to the P. O.

"Source Inspection by N.E.L. is required on this order prior to shipment from your plant. Please notify N.E.L. in sufficient time to allow for proper planning and scheduling of our source inspector."

VENDOR ANALYSIS AND RATING

Objective evidence of satisfactory quality will be used to determine the contribution made by vendors to our overall product quality. A perpetual record is maintained on the results of Receiving Inspection with reports issued to management when appropriate. Quality Engineering will collaborate with purchasing on any necessary action resulting from the receiving inspection records and vendor history.

The Quality Assurance Division will survey the capability of Vendors based on the following:

1. New supplier, critical/high dollar parts, special process
2. Quality history dictates survey is needed, problem vendor
3. Weak vendor, poor price and delivery, change in location or ownership

All surveys are arranged through purchasing with all information documented and filed in the Quality Engineering Department.

RECEIVING AND RECEIVING INSPECTION

All incoming materials and supplies shall be inspected upon receipt. The amount of inspection will be governed by the use and application of the items. All items designated to become a part of our Finished Product as delivered to the customer will be inspected by receiving inspection for conformance to the applicable purchase order, referenced drawings and/or vendor catalogues to which the material was purchased. Sampling inspection will be used per Mil STD 105 when appropriate and shall be limited to receiving inspection only. Any sample-Inspection/Testing shall be to a "Normal" 1.0% AQL acceptance except for hardware and similar type items where a 4.0% AQL will be used. Quality Engineering will govern any reduced or tightened inspection/tests.

Q.A. Procedures Manual

The following procedures shall be complied with:

1. Purchased Administrative Supplies, paper, etc.
   1.1 Receiving clerk shall verify item(s) against our p.o., count, check for damage, etc. and if in order and acceptable, complete and sign a receiving report and forward with items to the stock room or using department as necessary.
2. Purchased parts, components, etc.
   2.1 Receiving clerk shall verify item(s) against our p.o., count, check for damage, etc. NOTE: Cartons apparently damaged in shipment shall be immediately brought to the attention of your supervisor for claim and/or corrective action as appropriate. Complete and sign a receiving report and forward with items to Receiving Inspection Station.
   2.2 Receiving Inspector shall obtain the drawing, specification, and catalogue as referenced on the P. O. and visually inspect and test (when necessary) the items for conformance to the appropriate document(s) and to the General Inspection Check List. Electrical components purchased from approved, certified sources, i.e., Triplett, Weston/Daystrom, etc. as replacement parts, need not be electrically tested. Electrical components purchased for use in Nelson manufactured/assembled products for delivery to the customer shall be electrically tested per Mil STD. 105 to a 1% AQL—Normal Inspection—as appropriate.
   2.3 Receiving Inspector shall complete the Inspection portion of the receiving report, (sign or stamp and date) retain one copy for Inspection Records and forward remaining copies with acceptable material to the stock room or to the using department as applicable under specific circumstances.
   2.4 Discrepant material shall be red tagged, and segregated for immediate review with your supervisor for appropriate corrective action. Material to be returned to vendor shall be processed through purchasing for control. Material requiring an M.R.B. decision shall be so noted on the red tag. After decision has been made (return to vendor, use as it, rework, or scrap), with M.R.B. instructions noted on the tag, process material accordingly, complete the Receiving Report and red tag. Attach red tag to Receiving Inspection copy for Vendor History Record.
3. Customers' Equipment (meters, test equipment, for modifications, repairs and calibration)

3.1 Receiving clerk shall verify item(s) against customer P.O. or work order as appropriate.

3.1.1 The Receiving Record log shall be completed in detail including the Nelson work order tag number(s).

3.1.2 A work order tag shall be completed in detail and attached to each individual item.

3.1.3 Each piece of equipment shall be delivered to the shop supervisor for scheduling.

4. Customer furnished material for contract assembly work.

4.1 Receiving clerk shall verify item(s) and correct count against customer P.O. or work order as appropriate. If acceptable, the Receiving Report shall be completed in detail and forwarded with materials to assembly dept.

4.2 Any discrepancies shall be immediately referred to your supervisor for clarification with customer and/or corrective action as necessary.

5. Customer Returned Material

5.1 Receiving Clerk shall verify item(s) against Customer Rejection Report, verify count, check and note condition, complete and sign a Receiving Report and forward with item(s) to Receiving Inspection Station.

5.2 Receiving Inspector shall verify reason for return and immediately notify the Sales Division to convene the Material Review Board for appropriate decision, necessary work and corrective action. The Sales Division shall complete the Customer Returned Material Report in detail for appropriate review by the Director of Quality Assurance. A Request for Corrective Action form shall be initiated as appropriate on all customer returned material.

6. All material being returned to the Vendor shall have a "Rejected Material Notice" initiated and signed by the Inspector. This notice shall be signed by Quality Assurance and Purchasing. Two copies will be sent to the Vendor advising the Vendor of the problem(s) and requesting documented corrective action and the return of one copy within 15 days to N. E. L. as signed by the Vendor's Quality Control Manager.

7. Any rejected Government source inspected material shall be immediately reported to the cognizant Government representative who serves our Company. The material shall not be used without written authority from the Government and our Material Review Board.

Q.A. Procedures Manual

INSPECTION AND TEST

All items are inspected and/or tested at various stages as required by the "Quality Assurance Operation Route Tag" and/or other specific documented instructions as required by Engineering, Quality Assurance or the Customer. The selection of inspection/test stages for a specific unit is based on the following considerations as typical:

1. Compatibility with the normal manufacturing operations and the type of product.
2. Specific characteristics not available for final inspection must be verified at a given stage if covered up by the next operation.
3. Cost of replacing discrepant parts/assemblies found during final assembly, inspection or test.

Our Company utilizes the Quality Assurance Operation Route Tag for simplicity of operation and for cost effective control. The purpose of the Quality Assurance Operation Route Tag is to factually document which individual did what operation at a specific time and date and to instill in each person the basic fact that he/she is responsible for the quality of each part, function or service that they work on or perform. Each person who performs a specific operation must sign his/her name which will signify that he/she has performed the operation correctly to his/her satisfaction, in accordance with the drawing/sketch and/or the manufacturing plan of operation. Each person is charged with the following responsibilities as related to any job: **DO IT RIGHT THE FIRST TIME . . . . WORK IN A PLANNED, SYSTEMATIC MANNER . . . . . BE SURE, BE CONSISTENT, BE SATISFIED . . . . YOUR SIGNATURE MEANS ZERO DEFECTS.**

Procedure:

1. The Supervisor shall complete the upper portion of the tag. A tag shall be made for every job with multiple tags used as necessary to cover every operation.
2. The Operator shall: Punch time clock "on and off" for each operation; complete "operation—quantity—performed by sections" prior to releasing job for next operation. The Receiving Operator will not start his/her operation unless prior operation is signed off.
3. A **"First Piece Verification Inspection" MUST BE MADE ON EACH JOB** by the Supervisor or his designated representative just prior to signing his name and the date (Verified by and Date.) The Operator shall "self check his work" but **cannot verify the work.**
4. After First Piece Inspection, another operator may verify the work

in process as established by the Supervisor. All items shall be verified 100% for conformance to the standards. The Supervisor shall use the "Comments Section of the Tag" for instructions.

The Supervisor and/or Quality Assurance may tighten or require additional verification, depending on the critical nature of the parts and/or the job. All in process verification shall be recorded, initialed and dated by person verifying (i.e., 50-CLC.)

5. Any discrepancies shall be immediately reported to the **Supervisor** for prompt corrective action. All discrepancies shall be recorded by operation.
6. The Quality Assurance Inspector may "Random Sample" at any operation at any time. Any discrepancies shall be recorded by operation, immediately reviewed with the **Supervisor** with corresponding disposition and corrective action recorded as appropriate. The Inspector shall sign and date the "Quality Audit" Section.
   NOTE: MRB action will require customer concurrence.
7. Each tag shall be finally reviewed by the Supervisor and dated. The Supervisor shall review discrepancies with the operator(s) as appropriate for corrective action. The operator(s) shall sign and date, acknowledging the discrepancies.
8. Quality Assurance will audit or 100% inspect finished parts and packing depending on the Quality confidence level of the respective producing department.
9. No shipments are to be made unless Quality Assurance Operation Route Tag is signed off and dated by Quality Assurance as "O. K. to Ship."
10. All Quality Assurance Operation Route Tags must be turned in to the Quality Assurance office for review, analysis, posting and filing where appropriate. This tag is a permanent Quality record and shall be reviewed with management on a regularly scheduled basis.

All finished items receive 100% inspection/test for the following characteristics:

1. Workmanship, finish, marking, appearance.
2. Completed Quality Assurance Route Tag to assure all inspection/tes. have been accomplished.
3. Final Quality Assurance tests and inspections deemed necessary to assure acceptance of product which conforms to customer and/or N.E.L. specified Quality and Reliability standards as applicable.

Q.A. Procedures Manual

4. Calibration and certification as appropriate.
5. Preservation and packaging for compliance to required specifications, prior to releasing units for shipment.

All data associated with the item/order is filed as required per applicable specifications for timely retrieval and review.

NON-CONFORMING MATERIAL REVIEW

This Procedure describes the method for handling and reviewing materials, parts and assemblies which do not conform to specifications/drawings. This Procedure supplements the Receiving Inspection and Inspection/Test Sections of this Manual which cover discrepant material. It is not intended to conflict with inspection rejections where normal workmanship type rework can correct the discrepancies.

Discrepancies are defined under the following two classifications:

1. **Deviation:** Departure from requirements of the Contract, Specifications or the Drawing **which may adversely** affect safety, performance, weight, service or life of the article or adversely affect inter-changeability of parts or assemblies.
2. **Variation:** Departure from the requirements of the Contract, Specifications or the Drawings **which do not adversely** affect safety, performance, weight, service or life of the article or adversely affect inter-changeability of parts or assemblies.

Our Material Review Board has been established for the purpose of making decisions as to the disposition of discrepant material and consists of the following members:

1. Engineering Representative
2. Quality Assurance Representative
3. Manufacturing Representative
4. Customer/Government (When required)

The Inspector and/or any person detecting a discrepancy is responsible for rejecting and red tagging the item to preclude mixture or use pending disposition. The Chief Inspector will review the item(s) and convene the M.R.B., for final review and decision. All members of the Board must agree on the disposition. All decisions must be documented for future review concerning previous M.R.B. actions.

Whenever the Review Board decides to "Accept a Part with Deviation", the **Customer must be contacted** requesting approval of the deviation for use. Decisions made by the Review Board include:

Use as is; Rework; Return to Vendor; Scrap

All discrepant material awaiting disposition is secured and under the jurisdiction of Quality Assurance.

Any rework of non-conforming material shall be in accordance with the procedure which must be prepared by the Project Engineer and when required, as approved by the Customer.

Records of Material Review Board actions are maintained by Quality Engineering as previously described.

STOCK AND STORAGE CONTROL

The Quality Engineering Department conducts random audits of stock and storage areas on an unannounced basis. (An audit is conducted at least once every 60 days.)

The Quality Audit is made to assure conformance to the following as typical:

1. Stock room personnel do not accept material, parts, etc. for stocking/storage without proper evidence of acceptance by Inspection.
2. Materials, parts and assemblies are stored in a manner suitable to their physical characteristics to prevent damage, deterioration, corrosion and that protection is provided from dust, dirt, etc.
3. All stock is properly identified and that a first in—first out system is maintained.
4. Stock room is restricted to only authorized personnel.
5. Items having shelf life are identified and issued prior to expiration date.
6. Materials classified as chemicals, paints, solvents, etc. are plainly identified as "Inflammable"—"Corrosive", etc. and that such materials are stored in a suitable area.
7. Housekeeping and material handling is adequate and proper.

Quality Engineering will prepare and process a "Request for Corrective Action" when necessary to report findings or to remove items from stock for rework, repair or scrap, as applicable.

CUSTOMER INSPECTION AT N.E.L.

Our Customers are permitted to inspect/test their purchased items prior to delivery in accordance with the terms of their contract/purchase agreement when approved by the Executive Management of Nelson Electronics Laboratories, Inc.

This Customer Source Inspection is permitted to assist the Customer in determining conformance of the product to the specifications and contract requirements on items being shipped to outside locations and for audit or related reasons.

Specific documents and inspection/test data relative to the purchased item(s) will be made available to the customer at the time of source inspection when approved by N.E.L. Management.

CUSTOMER FURNISHED EQUIPMENT

When Customer furnished inspection/test equipment is provided to our Company for use on specific contracts, appropriate procedures will be written for the proper handling, storage and inspection of the equipment if required to be other than those currently in effect as described herein.

INSPECTION STAMPS

Quality Assurance is responsible for the procurement, issuance and control of all inspection/test stamps. Records will indicate the individual's name and assigned stamp number. Stamps will not be loaned to anyone for any reason. Damaged, lost or misplaced stamps will be reported to Quality Assurance immediately for necessary action. Persons transferring or leaving the company will return their stamps to Quality Assurance. These stamps will be withheld for a period of 90 days before re-issuance.

Quality Assurance will review all stamps on a random basis to assure legibility and for correct name and number.

TYPICAL EXHIBITS

Nelson Electronics Laboratories

Quality Assurance Procedures Manual

Control Log

No.	Name & Location	Date	Rev.	Rev.	Rev.
1	R.F. ERICKSON N.E.L.	2-66	1 7-68		
2	C.L. CARTER JR. N.E.L.	2-66	7-68		
3	CHARLES SHILLING N.E.L.	2-66	7-68		
36					
37					
38					
39					
40					
41					
42					
43					
44					
45					

QAPMCL-CLC-2/66

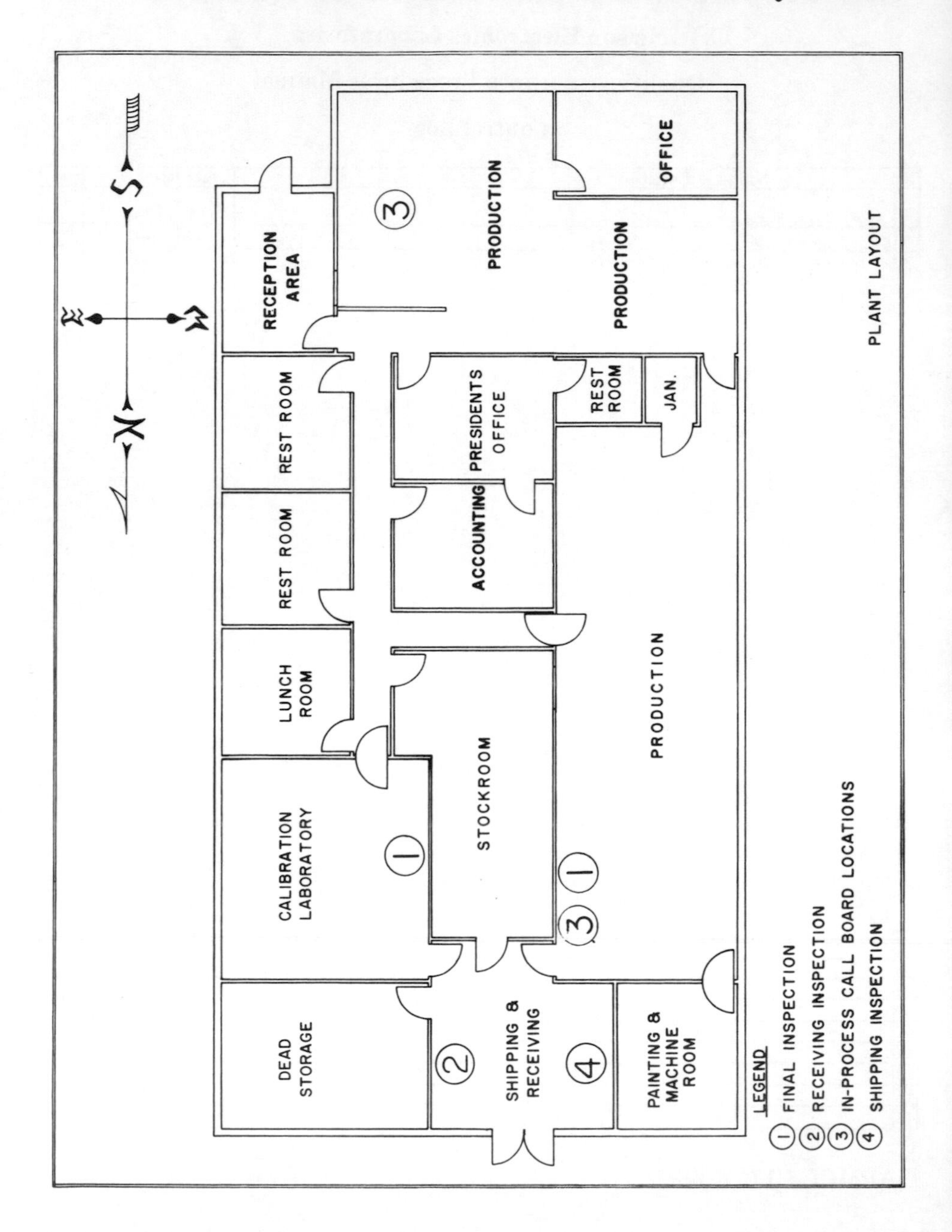

PLANT LAYOUT

TYPICAL INSPECTION FLOW CHART

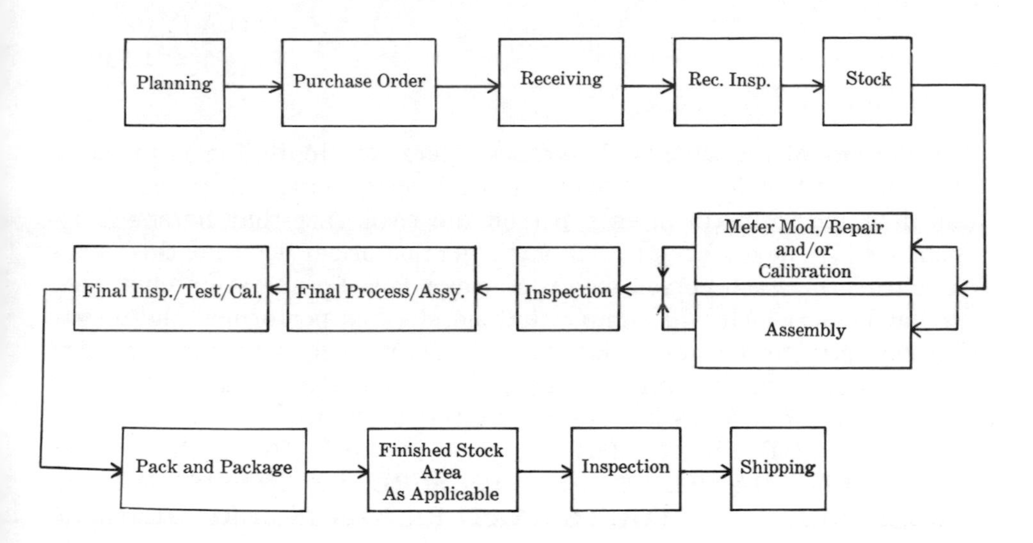

IFC-CLC-2/66

QUALITY ASSURANCE PROCEDURE

Title: "Quality Assurance Operation Route Tag"

Q.A.P. 102 Rev.
Date: 12-30-65

To All Operating Divisions:

The Purpose of the Quality Assurance Operation Route Tag is to factually document which individual did what operation at a specific time and date and to instill in each person the basic fact that he/she is responsible for the quality of each part, function or service that they work on or perform. Each person who performs a specific operation must sign his/her name which will signify that he/she has performed the operation correctly to his/her satisfaction, in accordance with the drawing/sketch and/or the manufacturing plan of operation. Each person is charged with the following responsibilities as related to any job: **DO IT RIGHT THE FIRST TIME . . . . . . WORK IN A PLANNED, SYSTEMATIC MANNER . . . . . . BE SURE, BE CONSISTENT, BE SATISFIED . . . . YOUR SIGNATURE MEANS ZERO DEFECTS.**

Procedure:

1. The Supervisor shall complete the upper portion of the tag. A tag shall be made for every job with multiple tags used as necessary to cover every operation.
2. The Operator shall: Punch time clock "on and off" for each operation; complete "operation—quantity—performed by sections" prior to releasing job for next operation. The Receiving Operator will not start his/her operation unless prior operation is signed off.
3. A **"First Piece Verification Inspection" MUST BE MADE ON EACH JOB** by the Supervisor or his designated representative just prior to signing his name and the date (Verified by and Date). The Operator shall "self check his work" but **cannot verify the work.**
4. After First Piece Inspection, another operator may verify the work in process as established by the Supervisor. All items shall be verified 100% for conformance to the standards. The Supervisor shall use the "Comments Section of the Tag" for instructions.

The Supervisor and/or Quality Assurance may tighten or require additional verification depending on the critical nature of the parts and/or the job. All in process verification shall be recorded, initialed and dated by person verifying (i.e. 50-CLC).

Q.A. Procedures Manual

5. Any discrepancies shall be immediately reported to the **Supervisor** for prompt corrective action. All discrepancies shall be recorded by operation.
6. The Quality Assurance Inspector may "Random Sample" at any operation at any time. Any discrepancies shall be recorded by operation, immediately reviewed with the **Supervisor** with corresponding disposition and corrective action recorded as appropriate. The Inspector shall sign and date the "Quality Audit" Section.
   NOTE: MRB action will require customer concurrence.
7. Each tag shall be finally reviewed by the Supervisor and dated. The Supervisor shall review discrepancies with the operator(s) as appropriate for corrective action. The operator(s) shall sign and date, acknowledging the discrepancies.
8. Quality Assurance will audit or 100% inspect finished parts and packing depending on the Quality confidence level of the respective producing department.
9. No shipments are to be made unless Quality Assurance Operation Route Tag is signed off and dated by Quality Assurance as "O.K. to Ship."
10. All Quality Assurance Operation Route Tags must be turned in to the Quality Assurance office for review, analysis, posting and filing where appropriate. This tag is a permanent Quality record and shall be reviewed with management on a regularly scheduled basis.

C. L. Carter Jr.

C. L. Carter, Jr.
Director, Quality Assurance

R. E. Erickson

R. E. Erickson,
Chief Executive Officer

C. D. Shilling

C. D. Shilling, Vice President,
Operations Manager, Plano

GENERAL INSPECTION CHECKLIST
WIRED ASSEMBLIES

Visual-Mechanical Inspection Shall be Accomplished Using Clean 4X Magnalite or Equivalent. Electrical Test Equipment Must be in Calibration.

TYPICAL ITEMS

1. No Loose Hardware, Parts, Sub-Assemblies, etc.
2. Correct Screws, Nuts, Washers, (Per Print.)
3. Name Plates, Markings and Decals Shall be Smooth (Wrinkle and Bubble Free.) Stampings, Screenings, etc. Shall be Intact, Legible and Ink Shall be Fungus Proof. (Pass Tape Test.)
4. Parts Free From Scratches, Fractures, Dents, Burrs.
5. Painted Surfaces Free From Scratches, Chips, Blisters.
6. All soldered Connections per Standard.
7. Solderless Terminals per Standard Using Only Specific Manufacturers Tools.
8. Wire Length and Routing Sufficient to Allow One Repair.
9. Cable and Wire Routing per Print, Tight Cable Lacing, No Pinched or Chaffed Wires, Wire and Cable Clear of Screw Threads and Sharp Edges.
10. Adequate Protection and Clamping of Cables.
11. No Spliced Wires (Unless Specified on Drawing or Approved by Engineering and Quality Assurance.)
12. No foreign Material. Units Shall be Clean, Inside and Out.
13. Completed Quality Assurance Route Tag.
14. Unit Calibrated and Properly Labeled.
15. Proper Packing, Packaging, Paper Work Completed.

INSPECT IN A PLANNED, SYSTEMATIC MANNER.
BE CONSISTENT, BE SURE, BE SATISFIED.

"YOUR STAMP MEANS ZERO DEFECTS"

Q.A. Procedures Manual

RECEIVING RECORD

DATE 19	PURCHASE ORDER NO.	RETURNED GOODS
RECEIVED FROM		PREPAID
ADDRESS		COLLECT
VIA	FREIGHT BILL NO.	

	QUANTITY	ITEM NUMBER	DESCRIPTION
1			
2			
3			
4			VOID - for use in
5			Quality Assurance
6			Procedures Manual
7			
8			
9			
10			
11			
12			

REMARKS: CONDITIONS, ETC.

NO. PACKAGES	WEIGHT	RECEIVED BY	CHECKED BY	DELIVERED TO

(FOR REFERENCE ONLY) BE SURE TO MAKE THIS RECORD ACCURATE AND COMPLETE

No. 89487 VOID

2R 260 Rediform ®

NELSON ELECTRONICS LABORATORIES, INC.

"REJECTED MATERIAL NOTICE"

Vendor ____________________ Date __________

P. O. No. ______________ Part No. __________ Job No. ______

Item No.	Quantity	Sample Qty.	Inspection Results

Inspector ______________

REQUEST FOR VENDOR CORRECTIVE ACTION

Please describe the corrective action taken to prevent like or similar discrepant material from being produced and/or delivered to our company. Complete and return one copy to the undersigned on or before __________ Your time and interest are appreciated.

NELSON ELECTRONICS LABORATORIES, INC.

Nelson Electronics Laboratories, Inc.

____

Director, Quality Assurance Date

____

Purchasing Agent Date

VENDOR CORRECTIVE ACTION

____

CLC 2/66 RMN-VCA Date and Signature of Vendor Quality Manager

Q.A. Procedures Manual

TYPICAL MATERIAL REVIEW REPORT

RECEIVING REJECTION ☐ LINE REJECTION ☐ OTHER ______ | JOB NO.

PART NO.		PART NAME		CONTRACT NO.	W.O. RUN NO. OR P.O. NO. & R.R.	
QUANTITY REC.	QUANTITY ACCEP'D.	QUANTITY INSP.	QUANTITY REJ.	INSP. BY	DEPT. OR VENDOR RESP.	
COMPLETE THROUGH:	OPER. SEQ.		DEPT.	MACH. GROUP	MACH. CLASS	MACHINE NO.
MATERIAL	DIMENSION	SPECIAL PROCESS	FINISH	DAMAGE	ASSEMBLY	

DISCREPANCIES:

Q.C. SUPERVISOR:

CORRECTIVE ACTION

PRODUCTION ☐ VENDOR ☐ OTHER ☐

CAUSE:

ACTION TAKEN:

PROD. SUPERVISOR | DATE

PRELIMINARY MATERIAL REVIEW DISPOSITION

REWORK ☐ SCRAP ☐ MRB ☐ USE AS IS ☐

RETURN TO VENDOR ☐ RECURRENCE YES ☐ NO ☐

INSTRUCTIONS:

Q.A. ENG.

DATE DATE

MATERIAL REVIEW BOARD

DISPOSITION & ACTION:

REWORK ☐ USE AS IS ☐ RET. TO VENDOR ☐ SCRAP ☐

INSTRUCTIONS:

Q.A. ENG. CUSTOMER

DATE DATE DATE

NELSON ELECTRONICS LABORATORIES, INC.

"REQUEST FOR CORRECTIVE ACTION"

Initiated by: ________ Quality____ Eng.___ Mfg.____ Sales____ Admin.

Name: ______________________________________ Date: __________

Directed to: ______________________________________ Dept: __________

Reply requested by: ______________________________________
Date

Corrective Action is requested as follows:
(Describe problem, cause, Job No., parts, Customer, etc.)

Corrective Action taken:

____
Name and Department Date

- -

_ Reviewed and Accepted

_ Requires MRB Action: __________ __________ __________
Q. A. Eng. Mfg.

_ Customer notified of Corrective Action
_ Yes _ No Date__________

(Complete in Duplicate: Retain Duplicate copy—
Original must be returned to Initiator on time)

CLC 2/66 RFCA

Q.A. Procedures Manual

NELSON ELECTRONICS LABORATORIES, INC.

"CUSTOMER RETURNED MATERIAL RECORD"

Procedure for Use:

This Customer Returned Material Record is to be completed in detail for every item returned by the customer regardless of reason. The receiving clerk will notify the Operating Manager immediately upon receipt of return of material. This record will be completed by the Operations Manager and jointly reviewed by the Director of Quality Assurance for analysis and corrective action. The Customer Returned Material Record is a permanent management record and is retained by the Director of Quality Assurance.

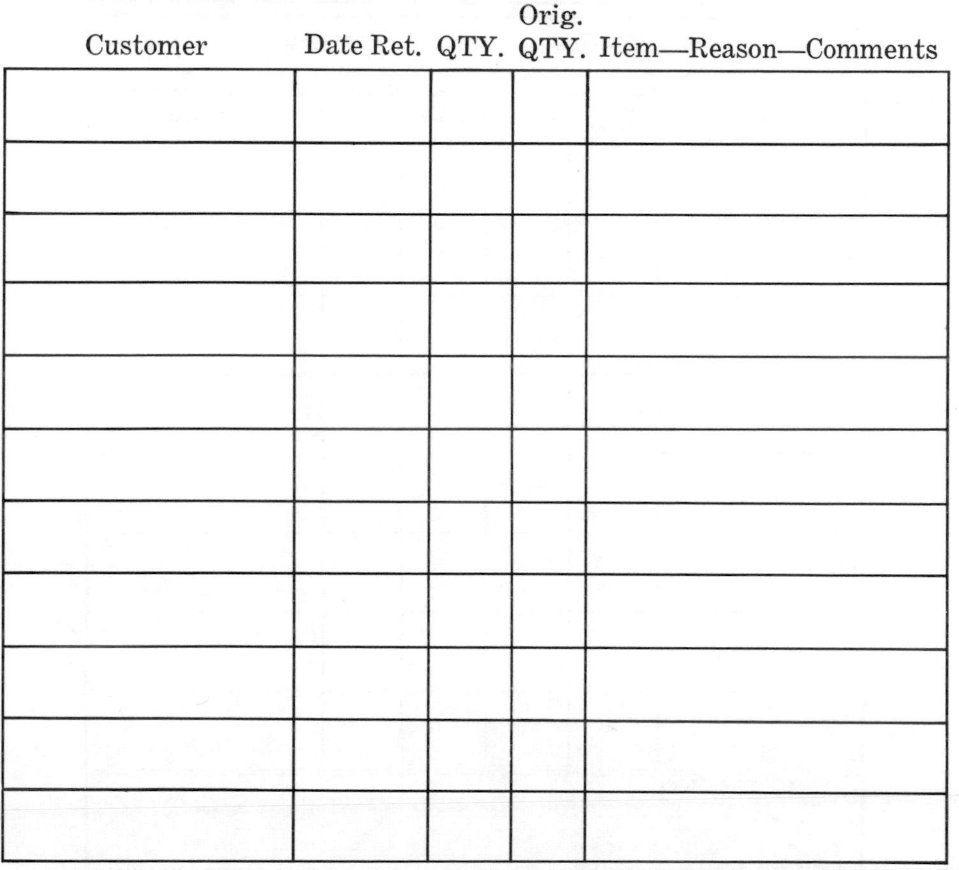

Customer	Date Ret.	QTY.	Orig. QTY.	Item—Reason—Comments

C.L.C. 2-66 C.R.M.R.

Q.A. Procedures Manual

Front

NELSON ELECTRONIC LABS, INC.

Quality Assurance Operation Route Tag

________________ Dept. Job No. ________ Qty. ________

Customer __________________________ Item __________

OPERATION	QTY.	PERFORMED BY	VERIFIED BY	DATE	QUALITY AUDIT	DATE	TIME & DATE
							ON
							OFF
							ON
							OFF

Rear

DISCREPANCY RECORD

OPERATION	NO. OF DISCREP.	REWORK	SCRAP	M. R. B.	REMARKS

CORRECTIVE ACTION:

REVIEWED BY: ________________________________

SUPERVISOR DATE OPERATOR DATE Q. A. DATE

Q.A. Procedures Manual

SPECIMEN COPY

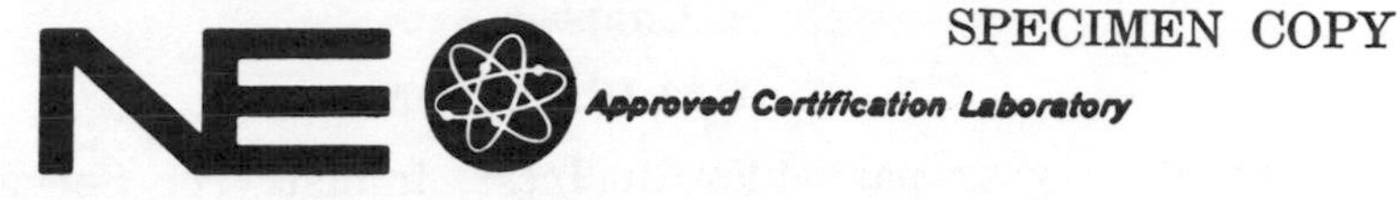

NELSON ELECTRONICS LABORATORIES, INC. • DALLAS NORTH RESEARCH PARK
1717 DALLAS NORTH PARKWAY • PLANO TEXAS

STANDARDS LABORATORY

REPORT OF CALIBRATION

16 March 1966

Reference: Fluke, M/803, S/N 1234, Customer P. O. 6789, and Test Number 12345

We hereby certify that the referenced item has been tested in our laboratory on the date and under the ambient conditions shown below; furthermore, that the limit of error found did not exceed that listed. Standards used and traceability to National Bureau of Standards standards are:

Reference #	Tolerance	Traceability	Last Certified
172	.05%	Ref. 101, 158, 177 and 178	8-19-65
158	.005%	NBS test 805465	8-19-65
101	.0001%	NBS test 803978	8- 6-65
177	.005%	NBS test 805467	8-16-65
178	.005%	NBS test 805466	8- 6-65

Uncertainty: .01%

Tested by:

C. D. Shilling
Operations Manager

DATE ______
TEMP. ______
HUMIDITY ______
TIME ______

Approved by:

R. E. Erickson
Chief Executive Officer

TYPICAL CALIBRATION LABEL

ITEM ______
SERIAL NO. ______ CAL. BY ______
DATE CAL. ______ DUE ______
ACCURACY ______
NELSON ELECTRONICS LABORATORIES INC.
DALLAS AD 5-1217 NE HOUSTON MO 6-1914

Q.A. Procedures Manual

Chapter 8

CALIBRATION

Based on your particular Business, Industry or Service Organization, there is an increasing need for using and maintaining accurate equipment. This is true in every organization including small machine shops; aircraft and aerospace corporations; communications firms; electronics firms of every description; space and scientific organizations; governmental agencies; hospitals, doctors and laboratories of all types; automobile manufacturers, dealers and service stations; or any firm utilizing computers or associated equipment.

We must develop confidence in the equipment, its accuracy, its stability, and we must have confidence in the organizations and the personnel who service and calibrate the tools, gages, test, inspection and laboratory equipment. How can a test be valid if we are not sure of the accuracy of the test equipment? To illustrate this point, I will use the following as a typical example: My doctor had the nurse test my heart, using electronic cardiograph test equipment. Prior to starting the test, I was able to look at the equipment and a manila tag which stated the equipment had been repaired on a particular date for "intermittent operation". After the test, I had a long chat with the doctor and asked about the "calibration of the equipment". He said he thought it was checked on a regular schedule, or possibly only when it displayed problems. He asked the head nurse, who stated that the typewriters and dictaphones were checked on a regular schedule, but that the Test Equipment Used on the Patients to Diagnose and Check Our Health Status were only checked when they didn't work, or when there were apparent problems with the equipment. I expressed my opinion concerning the need for confidence in the Test Equipment, and recommended a scheduled calibration and maintenance program to assure accuracy and confidence. I might add at this point that I have investigated the calibration of hospital equipment only to find that when I said "Calibration", the reply was "What's that?"

I would now suggest that the public challenge the accuracy, authority and validity of tests conducted on the status of your health. I would suggest that you ask three basic questions and obtain satisfactory answers.

(1) When was this equipment maintained and calibrated (month, day and year)?

(2) Who maintained and calibrated the equipment (company and name of individual)?

(3) When is the equipment due for re-calibration (month, day and year)?

I would suggest that the equipment should be "in calibration", with three months used as a reasonable calibration schedule. As an example: If they can show you a calibration record indicating the instrument was checked on 5-15-67, and your date of use was 7-15-67, I would suggest a reasonable confidence level in the instrument. If your date of use was 9-15-68, I would seriously question the confidence and accuracy of the instrument.

I am not suggesting anything that is not normally accepted in Good Quality Control Practices and Procedures. I **am** suggesting that there are Questionable Areas of Accuracy and Integrity of equipment in the highly professional areas of the medical field, including hospitals, clinics, doctors and laboratories who utilize electrical, electronic, pneumatic and other types of equipment and instruments. I **am** suggesting that all equipments, instruments, tools, gages and any piece of equipment used for Inspection, Testing, Analysis or Evaluation, be required by law (if necessary) to be calibrated and maintained at scheduled intervals.

I can qualify my personal knowledge and experience in the subject of Calibration by stating that "of the many hundreds of companies I have surveyed and evaluated during the past five or ten years, there were serious calibration problems, (i.e., items out of calibration, never calibrated, no records, no maintenance, etc.) in most all of the companies."

The lack of an effective calibration system as a part of the Quality Assurance Program is a major problem area which affects every Business, Industry, Profession and Consumer. How many times have you unknowingly paid for new spark plugs, points, condensers, etc., because of inaccurate, uncalibrated test equipment? How many people are taking unnecessary pills, based on a diagnosis made with inaccurate, uncalibrated test equipment? I know that new, electronic equipment is rejected on receipt due to inadequacies of calibration. This is a serious, costly problem.

With this in mind, I have taken the liberty to provide a "Typical Management Policy For A Calibration System" from which most all organizations can establish a cost effective Calibration System as appropriate to their needs. The resulting "Calibration System" must be an integral part of your Quality Assurance Program. The following is recommended to be used as a guide.

"Typical Management Policy For Calibration System"

1. **Scope:** This Policy provides for the establishment and maintenance of a cost effective Calibration System to control the accuracy of measuring and test equipment used to assure that supplies and services are in conformance with prescribed technical requirements affecting life, safety, quality, reliability, value and integrity of people, products and personal services. This Policy applies to all appropriate company organizations. There are no exceptions.

2. **General Requirements.** The Company shall establish and maintain a cost effective system for the calibration and control of all measuring and test equipment. The Calibration System shall be developed by the company's Quality Assurance Consultant or the Vice President or the Director of Quality Assurance and be approved by Executive Management. The system shall be coordinated with our Quality Assurance Program for cost effective control to provide adequate accuracy as related to the use of measuring and testing equipment. All equipment shall be covered by the system, whether used in our facilities or at another source. The system shall provide for the Prevention of Inaccuracy by timely detection of deficiencies, and immediate, positive corrective action as necessary. The system shall provide objective evidence of accuracy and conformance.

2.1 **Documented Description.** The company shall provide and maintain a written description of the Calibration System covering measuring and test equipment and measuring standards. The portion dealing with measuring and test equipment shall prescribe calibration intervals and sources. The description for calibration of measurement standards shall consist essentially of a listing of the applicable measurement standards, both reference and transfer, and shall provide nomenclature, identification number, calibration interval and source, and environmental conditions under which the measurement standards will be applied and calibrated. The description of the Calibration System and applicable procedures and reports of calibration shall be available to those who have the need to know.

2.2 **Adequacy of standards.** Standards established by the company for calibrating the measuring and test equipment used in controlling product quality shall have the capabilities for accuracy, stability, and range required for the intended use.

2.3 **Environmental controls.** Measuring and test equipment and measurement standards shall be calibrated and utilized in an environment controlled to the extent necessary to assure continued measurements of required accuracy giving due consideration to temperature, humidity, vibration, cleanliness, and other controllable factors affecting precision measurement. When applicable, compensating corrections shall be applied to calibration results obtained in an environment which departs from standard conditions.

2.4 **Intervals of calibration.** Measuring and test equipment and measurement standards shall be calibrated at periodic intervals established on the basis of stability, purpose, and degree of usage. Intervals shall be shortened as required to assure continued accuracy as evidenced by the results of preceding calibrations and may be lengthened only when the results of previous calibrations provide definite indications that such action will not adversely affect the accuracy of the system.

2.5 **Calibration procedures.** Written procedures shall be prepared or provided and utilized for calibration of all measuring and test equipment and measurement standards used to assure the accuracy of measurements involved in establishing product conformance. The procedures may be a compilation of published standard practices or manufacturer's written instructions and need not be rewritten. The procedures shall require that calibration be performed by comparison with higher accuracy level standards.

2.6 **Domestic calibration.** Measuring and test equipment shall be calibrated by the company or a commercial facility utilizing reference standards (or interim standards) whose calibration is certified as being traceable to the National Bureau of Standards, has been derived from accepted values of natural physical constants, or has been derived by the ratio type of self-calibration techniques. Reference standards requiring calibration by a higher level standards laboratory shall be calibrated by a commercial facility capable of providing the required service, or by the National Bureau of Standards. All reference standards used in the calibration system shall be supported by certificates, reports, or data sheets attesting to the date, accuracy, and conditions under which the results furnished were obtained. All subordinate standards and measuring and test equipment shall be supported by like data when such information is essential to achieving the accuracy and control required. Certificates or reports from other than the National Bureau of Standards shall attest to the fact that the Standards used in obtaining the results have been compared at planned intervals with the National Standard either directly or through a controlled system utilizing the methods outlined above. The company shall be responsible for assuring that the sources providing calibration services, other than the National Bureau of Standards, are in fact capable of performing the required service. All certificates and reports shall be available for review by those who have the need to know.

2.7 **Foreign calibration.** The provisions stated in Domestic Calibration shall apply with the exception that the National Standards Laboratories of countries whose standards are compared with International or U. S. National Standards may be utilized in lieu of the U. S. National Bureau of Standards.

2.8 **Application and records.** The application of the above requirements will be supported by records designed to assure that established schedules and procedures are followed to maintain the accuracy of all measuring and test equipment, and supporting standards. The records shall include a suitably identified individual record of calibration or other means of control for each item of measuring and test equipment and measurement standards, providing calibration interval and date of certification of results of last calibration. In addition, the individual record of any item whose accuracy must be reported via a calibration report or certificate will quote the report or certificate number for ready reference. These records shall be available for review by those who have the need to know.

2.9 **Calibration labeling.** Measuring and test equipment and measurement standards shall be labeled to indicate the date of last calibration, by whom it was calibrated, and when the next calibration is due. When the size or functional characteristics limit the application of labels, an identifying code shall be applied to the item to reflect serviceability and due date for next calibration. When neither labeling or coding is practical, the system shall provide suitable procedures for monitoring of recall records to assure adherence to calibration schedules. Labels, codes, or recall records for items which are not required to be used to their full capabilities, or items which require functional check only shall indicate the applicable condition.

2.10 **Control of supplier calibration.** The company shall be responsible for assuring that our suppliers have a Calibration System which essentially meets the requirements of this Policy. Quality Assurance will survey and audit our suppliers for control.

3. **APPROPRIATE DEFINITIONS.**

3.1 **Calibration.** Comparison of a measurement or instrument of known accuracy with another standard or instrument to detect, correlate, report, or eliminate by adjustment, any variation in the accuracy of the item being compared.

3.2 **Measuring and test equipment.** All devices used to measure, gage, test, inspect, or otherwise examine items.

3.3 **Measurement standard (reference).** Standards of the highest accuracy order in a calibration system which establish the basic accuracy values for that system.

3.4 **Measurement standard (transfer).** Designated measuring equipment used in a calibration system as a medium for transferring the basic value of reference standards to lower echelon transfer standards or measuring and test equipment.

3.5 **Interim standard.** An instrument used as a standard until an authorized standard is established.

TYPICAL GAGE RECORD

IDENTIFICATION NO.	TYPE	INSPECTION FREQUENCY

SECTION	BIN	DRAWER	DEPT.	TRAY

LOCATION

Specified Dimension	Actual Dimension	Pitch Diameter	Actual Diameter	Major Diameter	Actual Diameter	Minor Diameter	Actual Diameter	Date	Inspector	Amount of Wear

Front

GAGE RECORD

ACTIVE DATE

CALIBRATION CERT.
IDENT.__________
DATE__________BY__________
DUE__________SIZE__________
Reorder Tamper-Proof Labels #50 ULS100
From Deltronic, Box 2155, Costa Mesa, Cal.

INACTIVE DATE

Specified Dimension	Actual Dimension	Pitch Diameter	Actual Diameter	Major Diameter	Actual Diameter	Minor Diameter	Actual Diameter	Date	Inspector	Amount of Wear

REMARKS

Rear

By having a Calibration System as tailored to your needs, you can have the confidence you need in the Measuring, Testing, and Inspection Equipment, from initial phases of engineering design to the finished product. To have this confidence, you must have the functioning Calibration System in operation to assure Accuracy, Quality, Value and Integrity.

I wish to re-state my conviction that all equipments, instruments, tools, gages, and any piece of equipment used for Inspection, Testing, Analysis or Evaluation be required by law (if necessary) to be calibrated and maintained at scheduled intervals. Every company, firm, organization, hospital, laboratory, or whatever the function may be, should be required to have a documented and functioning calibration system for control, assurance, accuracy, and integrity.

THE CALIBRATION OF TOOLS, GAGES, EQUIPMENT AND PEOPLE

'Qualified People' are your most important asset, but 'People' are probably one of your greatest problems. The care and use of people is much like the care and use of tools, gages, and equipment. If you don't know how to care for and use them, they will be abused, ultimately ruined, and have to be reworked or replaced. Sometimes, good tools, good gages, good equipment, and good people are hard to replace. I believe everyone will agree that all of the above statements involve vast amounts of time and money. Therefore, we must have a clear understanding of the problems, causes, and corrective action associated with the calibration of tools, gages, equipment, and people. The calibration of tools, gages, equipment and people is not only a vital necessity in our complex society of business, industry, and government, but I believe, and I trust you will agree, that the calibration of tools, gages, equipment, and people is your most important project, program — and challenge!

The vital need for tool, gage, and equipment calibration is generally understood and highly recommended by professional quality managers, engineers, and technical personnel. Every quality and reliability system or program must have a good basic calibration system to assure the desired accuracy and long use of tools, gages, and equipment. We must calibrate in an area which is adequately controlled and conducive to accurate measurements. We must maintain adequate records for timely recall, calibration and repair history, and for traceability to the National Bureau of Standards, either direct, or through a qualified calibration laboratory. We must place a high degree of confidence in the calibration system because we must depend on the tools, gages, and equipment for manufacture, inspection, and testing of our products. The integrity of the product must be unquestionable. The quality of the product must be acceptable to all customers.

In reviewing the above statements, we should agree that the text of my thoughts is not really too complicated or complex. However, if you are in the normal business, industrial, or government organization today, you are probably faced with, and have major problems associated with, the calibration of tools, gages, equipment, and people.

The problems come in all shapes and sizes, just like good and bad shoes; good and bad electronic equipment; good and bad steel; good and bad automobiles; good and bad companies; qualified and unqualified people; and good and bad calibration systems, to name just a few examples. I am sure you could name many more.

I have several cliches which I use from time to time to make a point or to express myself. Two of these are as follows:

"The problem doesn't know the name of the company!"

"I just don't need those kind of problems!"

In both of these expressions, I describe in accurate words, my thoughts and feelings regarding many particular circumstances in which I become involved on a daily basis. I strongly suspect that each and every one of you could use these same phrases.

Let's examine some of the problems for clarity and general discussion.

A. Good shoes are attractive, wear well, and are comfortable; inferior shoes do not wear well and probably cause your feet to hurt.

B. Good electronic equipment performs as stated, is reliable and accurate, and is backed by a reputable firm — either new or old. Bad electronic equipment is of poor quality, poor reliability, poor design, and gives sub-standard performance.

C. Good cartridge case steel draws well and makes acceptable, quality shell cases. Bad cartridge case steel has hidden internal defects, poor surface quality, and substandard chemical and metallurgical characteristics, which prohibits the production of good cases.

D. Good automobiles provide reliable, safe transportation; are attractive; and display good workmanship. Substandard automobiles are consistently poor in performance, unreliable, and of poor quality.

E. Good companies are known for quality, reliability and integrity. It is a pleasure to do business with them; it is a pleasure to work for them. Other companies are 'bad news' for everyone concerned — their vendors, their customers, and their employees.

F. Qualified people make up good companies and provide good products and services, they are pleasant to work with — and sometimes hard to find. Unqualified people are problems for everyone, including themselves. They must want to learn and thereby be what I call 'trainable'. Our goal must be to 'qualify the unqualified'.

G. Good calibration systems will provide accurate tools, gages, equipment, and standards which assure good quality. Inferior calibration systems can destroy tools, equipment, products, companies — and people!

The following typical calibration schedules will give you some idea of what it takes to maintain accurate tools, gages, equipment, and standards.

TYPICAL INTERVALS OF CALIBRATION

	MAXIMUM
Test. Equipment used for Acceptance of Product and/or Calibration (Scopes, Bridge, Voltmeters)	6 Months
Standards, Primary	12 "
Standards, Secondary	6 "
Gage Blocks, Working	6 "
Gage Blocks, Master	12 "
Thermometers and Heat Controls	6 "
Micrometers, Calipers, etc.	1 "
Go/No-Go Gages	1 "
Wire Strippers, mechanical	1 "
Wire Strippers, automatic	Each setup, hourly, and random-piece audit.

The following typical orientation program (same as in Chapter 4) is suggested for use in communicating with and calibrating your people:

TYPICAL ORIENTATION AND INDOCTRINATION PROGRAM

TIME: One Hour — first day of employment or as pre-arranged for current personnel.

PLACE: Training room or quiet office.

EQUIPMENT: Flip chart; 16mm movie projector and screen; 35mm slide projector; and accessories such as:
- Display of company products
- Time clock (if used)
- Forms, as normally used
- Specific items of interest or use.
- Movies of company, company products
- Quality motivation film

PROGRAM LEADERS: Training Director
Industrial Relations Manager
Personnel Manager
Quality Assurance Director or Manager
Engineering Manager
Manufacturing Manager
Plus, any others whose participation may be vital to the orientation program.

REMEMBER: First impressions are often lasting impressions. This is an important program. **PEOPLE ARE YOUR MOST IMPORTANT ASSET.**

PROGRAM CONTENT:
1. Introduction of key management and personnel
2. Flip chart of company operation
3. Brief talk by department managers
   THEME: Communicate, Coordinate, Cooperate
   Training — Motivation
   Quality — Integrity
   Housekeeping — Safety, etc.
4. Movie on company, if available
5. Movie or slides on company products
6. Quality motivation film as presented and discussed by Quality Manager, stressing

'do it right the first time' program within the company.

7. Importance of teamwork — how the team functions — desired results
8. Questions and answers
9. Review significant items
10. Welcome to the company — and to the quality team.

The calibration of people is probably the most difficult to accomplish because it takes special people to make it work. We can calibrate people by recognizing the problems and then taking immediate constructive action. We can calibrate people by understanding them and working with them to solve their specific problems. We can calibrate people by training and motivation programs tailored to their needs. We can calibrate people by communicating, coordinating, and cooperating with them to the fullest extent possible. I have found that you can solve most of your customer quality relations problems by honest efforts in understanding each other's views — perhaps over a cup of coffee.

We must never forget that our goal is to produce quality products, at the lowest cost, with maximum profits for our organizations. We can accomplish and achieve our goals by the cost-effective calibration of tools, gages, equipment — and PEOPLE!

Chapter 9

PURCHASING

The Purchasing Organization should be dedicated to buying goods and services at the lowest total cost, on time, consistent with Acceptable Quality. Purchasing is responsible for achieving the above. If they do this, the company will receive value for the dollars expended.

This function requires individuals of the highest integrity. Profits can be increased, based on good sound buying ... many dollars can be lost, based on poor purchasing practices. Purchasing is a professional business requiring highly qualified, talented personnel and management. Vendor Quality Assurance is a supporting function to the Purchasing Organization. They assist Purchasing, and act as technical advisors and consultants. However, Purchasing is totally responsible for Buying and Obtaining the Best Products at the Lowest total Cost for the company.

I do not believe in Quality's dictating to Purchasing as to which vendors to buy from. Quality Assurance should advise and recommend, as based on factual evidence and results. Purchasing makes the decision — Right or Wrong.

I have been privileged to study the Purchasing Functions of many hundreds of Small, Medium, and Large companies. Many of them are the largest in the world. Many companies are utilizing computers in Purchasing Functions and, in effect, they are buying what the computer says they need; when they need it; and, which vendor has the best Price, Delivery, and Quality. Inaccurate data in a computer could cause, and has created manufacturing catastrophies! Quality Assurance plays a very important part in the use of computers, as do the Purchasing and Accounting Departments. We discuss computers in several chapters.

Some companies talk a good game about their Value Engineering, Cost Reduction, and Cost Effectiveness Programs, but too many of them do not practice what they preach. I can illustrate this by citing several examples of where major corporations, dealing principally in Government Contracts, have spent an estimated $100.00 to purchase a sole source item which they could have purchased for the cost of writing and mailing a $3.00 check. Instead of going the recommended cost-effective way, they issued a Request for Quotation, which had to be completed, returned, and processed. A purchase order was then issued for the $3.00 item, which was mailed within 24 hours; along with five copies of the invoice, which had to be processed for the check to be written and processed. This isn't cost effective for the Vendor or the Vendee, but it happens daily.

Some Purchasing Organizations utilize the telephone effectively in placing emergency orders for supplies and materials needed to meet schedules, or support the production lines. On the other hand, some of them will call long distance for a $4.00 book, and then follow up with a purchase order, which must be processed at considerable cost to everyone. I would recommend periodic Value Analysis Audits on the Purchasing practices and procedures utilized by the company. The Purchasing Department should have standard operating policies and procedures. Many, many dollars can be saved by well-informed Purchasing Management and Personnel. Our tax and defense dollars can be more effectively dispensed to provide everyone concerned with maximum Quality, Value, and Integrity, by utilizing the efficiency and cost effectiveness obtained by having a functioning Total Quality Assurance Program in concert with a well managed Purchasing Function.

To illustrate this point, it is the practice of many firms to issue a check for the small dollar item. Both the Vendor and the Vendee save time and money when this practice is followed. Some companies will request shipment C.O.D. and pay all charges based on cost effective savings they obtain in this manner, rather than starting the purchasing paper mill and misusing company or government funds. My records indicate there is much room for improvement in Purchasing, on both the company and government levels. Too many dollars are spent in unnecessary paper work.

With reference to Government Purchasing, my study indicates a vital need for unification and standardization of Purchasing functions. Every branch of the Government operates in a different manner. The Army, Navy, Air Force, NASA, and the many other independent agencies are all trying to retain "Individual Status", and thereby are all using Individual Purchasing Practices and requiring Individual Quality and Reliability Requirements as they feel necessary. This "Individual Attitude" creates ridiculous costs, and causes fantastic problems for the company trying to obtain or satisfy the contract. Using the term "Red Tape" is mild in some of the Government Purchasing and Contract Administration practices and procedures. This can be illustrated by saying "the weight of the unnecessary paper work in many,

many cases far exceeds the total weight of the finished item being purchased." The costs involved in doing business with the Government is often the reason given by companies for not wanting Government business.

On the other hand, there are "Open Purchase Orders" with little if any Quality requirements invoked, issued by "Individual Agencies" for materials, items and services to be provided on flight connected hardware. In many cases, the cognizant Government agency does not have qualified personnel conducting Quality Assurance and Inspection services.

The Defense Contract Administration Service was outstanding in theoretical terms as a means to unification of this portion of the Services. The theory is fine, but in practice it has created many unsolved problems, friction and unqualified personnel — half-heartedly trying to do a job for which they have not been trained. Some training is being accomplished. There is much to do. The Government Quality Assurance Representatives serve as the basic inspection agency for most all Government Contracts. These people have a great responsibility for accepting or rejecting millions of dollars in all types of goods, materials, and assemblies. The DCASR function is now a management system for auditing contractors. As such, DCASR personnel should be trained, motivated, and educated to allow them to make management decisions. A cost effectiveness study would prove to be very beneficial to the Government, the Companies, and to the Taxpayers.

In my opinion, the tragedy in our Space Program can be attributed to inadequate Purchasing and Contract Administration, inadequate and ineffective Quality and Reliability efforts by everyone concerned, and a general lack of Personal and Product Integrity. It has been reported that there were over 5,000 engineering changes made after the Apollo tragedy. This costly after the fact example should remind everyone of the need for up front — before the fact — Preventative Quality Efforts.

We **must** concentrate and re-dedicate our efforts to achieve Quality, Value, and Integrity.

The Purchasing organizations are the "Heart" of most all companies who rely on outside vendors as their main sources of supply. Many companies today purchase 50, 60, and 70% of the product they are manufacturing. This may consist of screws, nuts, iron, steel, aluminum, wire, clamps, solder, tools, component parts such as resistors, capacitors, integrated circuits, printed wiring boards, lugs, terminals, transformers, meters, radios, and many other items. All of your paper, forms, business equipment and associated items connected with operating any organization is obtained principally through the purchasing function of the company. Cost effective Purchasing is vital to the operation of any organization.

Many of your major corporations involved in the Aerospace, Aircraft, and Communications industries are "Huge Assembly Plants" in which the Purchasing Department buys most all of the items in one form or another. The Manufacturing Assembly department assembles all of the purchased items to complete the finished product which might be a Missile, a Jet Aircraft, or a complete communication system. Purchasing may then arrange to have the finished product delivered to the customer. Yes, Purchasing is a mighty big member of the Quality Team. Purchasing, Engineering, Manufacturing, Quality, and Accounting must work very closely together to assure on-time delivery of products with Quality, Value, and Integrity. It takes a total quality team effort, along with maximum communication, coordination, and cooperation.

Large corporations have many Buyers in their Purchasing Departments. The Buyers will usually specialize in particular items or product lines. As an example, one Buyer may be responsible for Resistors, Capacitors, Integrated Circuits, and Transformers. Another Buyer may be responsible for all Hardware items. Another will be responsible for "Engineering Purchasing" which involves supporting the desires of the engineering department. This is quite a task!

Smaller companies may have one or two Buyers who support the needs of the entire company.

Some of the largest commercial purchasing organizations are to be found in the Department Store type firms such as: Sears, Montgomery Ward, Penneys, and the associated independent type Chain Department Stores. All of these stores rely on Purchasing to Buy Goods and services from Vendors all over the world. The products are purchased "Wholesale" for the best price, delivery, and quality. The products must then arrive at the right store at the right time to coincide with coordinated sales and marketing efforts.

The principles of Price, Delivery, Quality, Value, Safety, Service, and Integrity apply as much to Department Store Purchasing, if not more than, to other types of Businesses. Communication, Coordination, and Cooperation are of the utmost importance. Configuration control over "who made what product" is of prime concern to those companies who sell on the basis of "Satisfaction Guaranteed or Your Money Back." They must have tight control over their vendors and this can be illustrated by looking at some of the items purchased from the companies mentioned. You may notice a blanket with a permanently attached tag which reads "Source No. 1234." Or, you may note a small tag on the inside pocket of your sport jacket "Vendor No. 74."

These, of course, are for configuration control should the item be defective or returned for cause. Valuable Vendor History can be obtained from simple configuration control by identifying each Vendor and having the Vendor mark his own product.

Some of the commercial firms have taught the government, military, and industrial firms a lot about good Quality and Configuration Control. But then, we all learn something new every day; and as you can see, it pays to be aware of "What's Going On" around you on a day-to-day basis for you never know when you can apply proven Quality Assurance techniques to a new company, a new product, or a new service.

The National Association of Purchasing Management is the Professional Purchasing Association which establishes the Code of Ethics to which members shall comply. This Association and affiliated organizations around the country are dedicated to the Price, Delivery, Quality philosophy, and I feel sure all members stand ready to serve the needs of Business, Industry, Government, and the Public by obtaining and providing Quality, Value, and Integrity for their employers and customers.

Professional Purchasing, Professional Value Engineering, and Professional Vendor Quality Assurance are "Key Professional Positions" on the Total Quality Assurance management team. Professional talent is truly the key to a successful team, whether it be baseball, football, or management.

THE PURCHASE ORDER

The Purchase Order does not have to be complicated with fine print that you can't read and do not understand. On the contrary, the Purchase Order should be simple, clear, and relate exactly what you want, when you want it, the price, quality and reliability requirements, and other typical items as related to your needs.

The Purchase Order can also be used as your receiving inspection report and should be utilized to your greatest advantage for cost effective paper work and vendor control. Do not create unnecessary paper work. Always combine and condense paper work for clear understanding, maximum value, and use.

Purchase Orders may be pre-numbered if you feel this is necessary for better control. However, simple control can be obtained with a Purchase Order Log Book or other similar control techniques. Use the method that best fits your organization structure. However, keep it simple, because complicated paperwork costs you money in more ways than you can imagine.

Although Purchase Orders vary from company to company, the sample which is included here may give you some idea as to the typical content of a Purchase Order. I prefer to combine the Purchase Order and Request for Quotation and Request for Proposal, based on cost-effective use of one widely used form. As noted, this form may also be used as your Receiving and Inspection Report.

C. L. Carter, Jr. and Associates, Inc.
MANAGEMENT AND PERSONNEL CONSULTANTS
401 Braniff Bldg. — Exchange Park
DALLAS, TEXAS 75235
AC 214 - 352-8019/8851

DATE ________________
NUMBER ________________

( ) PURCHASE ORDER ( ) REQUEST FOR QUOTE ( ) REQUEST FOR PROPOSAL

TO: ____________________

FOR THE FOLLOWING:

ITEM NO.	QUANTITY	DESCRIPTION	UNIT PRICE	TOTAL PRICE	DELIVERY REQ'D BY

NOTES:

1. The vendor must have a documented and functioning program for the control and assurance of quality, per ASQC Standard C-1, as acceptable to a professional quality survey by an independent agency and/or our company.
2. Acknowledge this order by returning one signed and dated copy to the undersigned within three days.
3. State and local taxes will be added as required.
4. Invoice in duplicate to Accounts Payable Department.
5. If you have any questions, please contact the undersigned immediately.
6. Terms: We honor discounts first; stated terms; otherwise, Net, 30 Days.

Q.C. Inspection: ( ) Accept ( ) Reject
( ) 100% Insp. ( ) Sample per 105
Mat'l. Review Disposition:

Inspected by: ____________ Date: ____________ Director of Purchasing ____________

Purchase Order Acknowledged By: ____________________ Date: ____________

Chapter 10

VENDOR QUALITY ASSURANCE

A very important part of the Total Quality Assurance Program is the Vendor Quality Assurance effort. This vital function provides assurance to all company Management (with particular emphasis on Purchasing, Procurement, Manufacturing, and Quality), that the Vendor, Supplier or Sub-contractor, as the case may be, is capable of producing what you ordered, and can be relied upon to deliver 'on schedule' at the 'agreed to' cost.

Adequate control of procurement sources is mandatory for all types of Businesses and Industries, in order to assure Price, Delivery, and Quality.

Vendor Quality Assurance requirements are invoked in many different ways. They can be stipulated in the contract via a specification, such as the A.S.Q.C. Standard C-1; MIL-Q-9858; MIL-I-45208; NASA 200 Series, etc., or they may be covered in the terms and conditions portion of the Actual Purchase Order. In either case, the vendor must comply with the requirements as appropriate to the items being purchased. Many of the companies establish and invoke their own specifications, which gives them specific control over their vendors. As an active member of the Vendor-Vendee Technical Committee of the American Society for Quality Control, I can assure the reader that there are many problems associated with having a "Multitude of Similar but Different Specifications." The many different Government Specifications which require Systems and Programs for the control of Quality and Reliability when combined with supplementary company documents, are enough to make life miserable for Quality Managers.

As you have read, in an effort to unify these Specifications and Documents, the Vendor-Vendee Technical Committee has generated the new Universal Quality Specification as covered in chapter 6 as titled, "Universal Quality Program Requirements." I recommend that you use the contents of the C-1 Standard for cost-effective Vendor Quality Assurance.

In addition, I am providing you with a typical company specification which can also be used to satisfy "Quality Assurance Requirements for Vendors". This is to be used as a guide and for reference information. I want you to have as much reference information in order to acquaint you with specific cases as used by business, industry, and government.

"QUALITY ASSURANCE REQUIREMENTS FOR VENDORS"

This specification establishes the requirements for a basic Quality Control Program to which the vendors of Nelson Electronics Laboratories, Inc. shall comply.

Vendors who furnish equipment, materials and/or appropriate services shall maintain a documented and functioning system for the control of quality which is acceptable to the Quality Assurance Division of Nelson Electronics Laboratories, Inc.

Any and all changes to this specification must be approved by Engineering and Quality Assurance management via a documented and controlled change order. The approvals and latest revision are shown below.

Q.A.P. — 101

Original Prepared By	Date	Engineering	Date	Quality Assurance	Date
C. L. Carter, Jr.	2-66	C. D. Shilling	3-9-66	C. L. Carter, Jr.	3-9-66

Rev.	Prepared By	Date	Description	Approvals	Date
A	CLC	6-68	ADD 16 & 17 AND MAKE MINOR CORRECTIONS	Eng. C.D.S. Q.A. C.L.C.	6-68
				Eng. Q.A.	
				Eng. Q.A.	
				Eng. Q.A.	
				Eng. Q.A.	
				Eng. Q.A.	
				Eng. Q.A.	
				Eng. Q.A.	
				Eng. Q.A.	
				Eng. Q.A.	
				Eng. Q.A.	

QUALITY ASSURANCE REQUIREMENTS FOR VENDORS

1. **Organization and Control**
   The vendor shall provide and maintain a system for the control and assurance of quality which will assure compliance with drawings, specifications, or other contractual provisions. The vendor's quality control system shall provide for the prevention and ready detection of discrepancies, for timely and positive corrective action and meet the other requirements of this document.
2. **Procedures**
   The vendor shall provide and maintain written procedures for the control of quality throughout all phases of contract performance. Written work and inspection instruction shall be provided as required to supplement drawings and specifications.
3. **Surveillance, Source and Resident Inspection**
   Nelson Electronics Laboratories shall have the right to survey the vendor's facilities, to inspect products, witness inspection and test and evaluate the Quality Control System, which may also extend to vendor's source of supply. Nelson Electronics Laboratories shall also have the right to maintain continuous source inspection and/or audit at the vendor's facilities.
4. **Control of Supplies and Suppliers**
   The vendor is responsible for assuring that all supplies and services conform to the contract requirements whether manufactured or processed by the vendor or procured from his vendors. The selection of sources, and the nature and extent of control, including both vendor incoming inspection and vendor surveillance, shall be the quality evidence furnished by the vendor and his demonstrated ability to perform in the specialized field involved. The vendor shall assure that applicable requirements are properly included or referenced on all subcontracts for supplies ultimately to apply on this contract.
5. **Quality Control Records**
   The vendor shall maintain adequate inspection records covering all phases of procurement, manufacture, test, calibration, tool controls, material (Chem-Phys) certifications, corrective action, and other records of quality control activities. Unless otherwise stipulated, these records shall be retained by the vendor for the period

of contract performance. Final acceptance records shall be retained for a minimum period of three years after completion of contract. These records shall be made available to Nelson Electronics Laboratories upon request.

6. **Drawing and Change Control**

The vendor shall maintain procedures and a system for control of drawings and drawing changes to assure that the latest applicable engineering drawings, specification requirements and contract change information will be available at the proper time in manufacturing, inspection or test. All obsolete information must be removed from all points of issue and use.

When the vendor is manufacturing to Nelson Electronics Laboratories specifications, no changes shall be made unless specifically authorized by the contract.

7. **Inspection and Test Equipment**

The vendor shall provide, maintain and calibrate inspection and testing equipment periodically against suitable higher standards, traceable to the Bureau of Standards. Procedures including positive tool and gage identification traceable to records and schedules for calibrating and maintaining inspection/test equipment must be maintained. Any tools used as media of acceptance inspection shall be classified and treated as gages. Tools and/or articles shall be inspected prior to release for production use and at established intervals. The vendor's inspection and testing equipment shall be made available for usage by authorized customer personnel to determine conformance with contracted requirements.

8. **Material Review, Control of Discrepant Material**

Material Review is defined as that process by which disposition of nonconforming material is determined, approved and recorded. The vendor shall provide for Material Review Board action on nonconforming supplies and retain records thereof including corrective action to preclude recurrance of discrepant materials. All nonconforming material shall be positively identified and removed from the normal production flow until disposition is complete. The Material Review Board shall consist of:

a. Quality Control Representative
b. Engineering Representative
c. Customer Representative when Required

Vendor's material review authority is limited to variations which:

(1) will not affect performance, interchangeability, weight, service life or safety, (2) will not adversely affect the reliability of the article, or (3) will not otherwise violate contract specifications. All other variations will require specific approval via Nelson Electronics Laboratories with items appropriately identified. Nelson Electronics Laboratories shall have the right to reject any nonconforming supplies which have been accepted by the vendor's Material Review Board.

9. **Special Processes**

Special processes are defined as those manufacturing processes where uniform conformance to the requirements cannot be assured by inspection of the articles alone or require destructive testing. These processes include, but are not limited to, fusion and resistance welding, soldering, printed wiring, plating, finishing, metallurgical/chemical cleaning and bonding, and such inspection processes as radiography, ultrasonic test, liquid penetrant and magnetic particle. The vendor and his lower-tier vendors shall maintain defect prevention process control of all special processes. These controls shall include the use of process control procedures, training and qualification of personnel. Records of certifications of processes, equipment or personnel shall be available for review by Nelson Electronics Laboratories.

10. **Nelson Electronics Laboratories Supplied Materials**

When material is furnished to the vendor, the vendor's procedures shall contain at least the following:

a. Examination on receipt, to the extent practicable, to detect damage in transit.
b. Inspection for completeness and proper type.
c. Care to insure adequate storage conditions.
d. Functional testing to determine satisfactory operation.

When furnished material is found damaged, malfunctions or otherwise unsuitable for use, the vendor shall furnish a report describing the nonconforming condition to the Nelson Electronics Laboratories representative.

11. **Material Control**

Material shall be identified from its receipt at the vendor's facility through delivery to the customer, so that operations, inspections or tests will not be omitted or misapplied. A method of stamping the material and/or tags or routing cards is the preferred means to be used by inspection and test personnel.

The vendor shall control all preservation, packaging, packing, shipping and handling to assure that all materials are adequately protected during all phases of contract performance.

Raw material furnished by the vendor or to be used in fabrication or processing of products shall conform to the applicable chemical, physical and other technical requirements. Evidence of this conformance shall be maintained by the vendor and or furnished to Nelson Electronics Laboratories when requested.

12. **Corrective Action**

The vendor shall take positive and prompt corrective action on defects when discovered by the vendor or Nelson Electronics Labs. When Nelson Electronics Laboratories sends the contractor a letter requesting corrective action, it is necessary that the vendor reply stating the steps taken to correct the problem. Nelson Electronics reserves the right to terminate any open orders until suitable corrective action is taken.

13. **Sampling Inspection**

No sampling may be used without procedures for application or administrative control. Any acceptance sampling procedure employed by the contractor shall be subject to Nelson Electronics Laboratories disapproval. Either MIL-STD-105 or MIL-STD-414 is generally acceptable. Sampling inspection as employed by the vendor does not relieve the vendor of his responsibility for items found defective.

14. **Proprietary Information**

Proprietary information, furnished by Nelson Electronics Laboratories to vendors shall not be disclosed to any one other than those who need to know in order to perform duties related to the particular Nelson Electronics Laboratories purchase agreement. Vendors shall assume the responsibility for any proprietary information.

15. **Workmanship**

Workmanship shall be of a consistently high level of quality commensurate with the state of the art as it exists during the term of the contract.

The vendor shall maintain adequate controls to ensure acceptable workmanship and acceptable quality levels. These controls shall be supported by definite acceptance criteria and appropriate documented workmanship standards and work instructions. Personnel shall be appropriately trained to perform in accordance with the workmanship standards and work instructions. Workmanship standards shall be subject to Nelson Electronics Laboratories disapproval. Depending on the contract, Nelson Electronics Laboratories may furnish workmanship standards to which the vendor shall comply.

16. **Guidance Documents**

The following documents of the latest issue, may be used as a guide in formulating your Quality Program or Inspection System:

A. MIL-Q-9858: Quality Program Requirements
B. MIL-I-45208: Inspection System Requirements
C. ASQC Standard C-1: General Requirements for a Quality Program
D. MIL-C-45662: Calibration System Requirements
E. NASA Documents: NPC 200-2 or NPC 200-3
F. Quality Assurance Workmanship Standards Manual by Carter

17. **Communication, Coordination, Cooperation**

Each vendor is requested to communicate, coordinate and cooperate with our company Purchasing and Quality Departments for Cost Effectiveness, Quality, Reliability, Value and Integrity. We consider our vendors to be a vital part of our Total Quality Team. Total teamwork is necessary from everyone and we will work with our vendors to obtain Quality Products and Services, on time, at the lowest total cost. However, we will not establish the vendor's quality program, nor do the work that is rightfully the responsibility of the vendor's management team.

Q.A.P. 101 Rev. A

VENDOR SURVEYS

Vendor Quality and Management Evaluation Surveys are used to develop a confidence level in the Vendor's ability to provide Quality Products and Services—on time at the stated cost. The Surveys must be made by qualified, knowledgeable individuals who have been adequately trained in evaluating Vendors, their Quality Programs, Special Processes and Management. The Survey, when conducted by qualified personnel, is an "Early Warning System," which should be used as a guide in evaluating the Vendor's capabilities.

There are many pro's and con's concerning the validity of Vendor Surveys as a means of predicting the receipt of acceptable products. There are those who have conducted so-called "studies" covering the

Vendor Quality Surveys conducted by two large corporations. The conclusions drawn by the "studies" indicate no correlation between the majority of the surveys and the incoming product quality. I challenged the "studies", based on a sample of two corporations, as being inadequate, along with the well-known inadequacies of unqualified personnel conducting Vendor Surveys. My written challenge has not been answered.

We must recognize the vital need for "Professional Quality Personnel" if we want a Professional Job done. You still cannot send "a Boy to do a Man's job." Management must recognize the Basic Facts of Life concerning qualified Vendor Quality Assurance Personnel. They must recognize that Unqualified Personnel will provide unqualified data . . . which will result in "Bad News" when the Vendor's product reaches receiving inspection. They must also realize that the individuals they send to conduct the surveys are Representing the Management of their companies. I can assure management that Poor and Inadequate Data obtained on Vendor Surveys can be directly attributed to Unqualified Personnel who do not know where to look . . . nor do they know what they are looking for. I am afraid there are too many cases which are best stated by saying, "The martinis were good, but I'm not sure if we really went through their plant." or "I'm not sure of what they can do." or "I guess they can do the job."

The "Unprofessional Surveys" have caused Vendor Quality Surveys to be the subject of great controversy. Management can benefit by taking positive, corrective measures to have only Professional Quality Personnel conduct Professional Vendor Surveys for accurate and timely data. Then, and only then, will Management have a Professional Early Warning System from which timely Purchasing decisions can save Management many, many dollars and headaches.

It has taken a long time and a great deal of hard work by Professional Vendor Quality Personnel to motivate and stimulate Purchasing Organizations to the point of realizing what Professional Vendor Surveys can do for them. We must continue our work for the Purchasing Organizations, by developing their confidence in Professional Quality Personnel who are dedicated to Price, Delivery, Quality, and Value.

A typical Vendor Quality Survey and Evaluation form has been provided for guidance, direction, and general information to be obtained by Professional Quality Personnel.

You will note that the form is simple, direct, and provides basic but necessary information for Quality, Purchasing, and associated management organizations. The simple rating scale is functional and provides a numerical measure by specific area. We must always be fair in our assessment of another man's shop and capabilities. That's why it's so important to have the surveys conducted by professional quality personnel who are knowledgeable in and understand the basic principles and philosophies of price, delivery, quality, safety, service, and integrity.

We must also be aware of the many companies who are only interested in the "order" and not too interested in whether they can produce a quality product, on time, at the agreed-to price. In many of these companies, we can blame it on plain and simple ignorance on the part of management, as to what they signed and agreed to. We can only hope and trust that the management of such companies will take the time to learn, before they go out of business. In many other companies where we find the "I don't care" attitude, we can only hope that they go out of business before they do too much damage to business, industry, and government customers.

VENDOR SURVEYS

Your Early Warning System

Vendor and management evaluation surveys are generating considerable interest and discussion. Since such surveys, when conducted by experienced, talented, professional personnel, constitute an Early Warning System, knowledge of their advantages can be highly beneficial.

If we are to manufacture our products at the lowest cost, on time and at a consistently acceptable level of quality, reliability and value, we must be able to "see up front" as far and as fast as possible to allow us to recognize and evaluate potential problem areas. Industries and people have one thing in common—no two are alike. Even the many companies producing similar end products do not build their items in the same manner because management, machines, people, purchasing and quality systems/programs are different.

Basically, more than simple differences are involved. We must ask some pertinent questions before becoming deeply involved with a vendor.

What do we know about him? Have we ever done business with

him? How long ago? Is the previous history good or bad? Was the same product or process involved? Is management the same? How much is this order worth? What's the risk? And, of course, there are many more.

There are many reasons for you to take a hard look: you may know little or nothing about the vendor or you, as the contractor, may be responsible for vendor output.

Whether you work for commercial, military or NASA buyers, it's just good common sense to know your vendor, thus increasing your confidence in his ability to consistently deliver an acceptable product —on time and at the lowest cost. All vendors **need not** be looked at, especially if good quality histories are on record. If you do have a history, use it to your benefit to reduce your receiving inspection costs. Put all the confidence you can in your vendor based on sound quality history or on an objective vendor and management evaluation survey and product audit.

If you have no vendor history, what should you look for when you arrive at his plant?

An ASQC vendor-vendee committee study shows that most companies look for the same basic survey information. Company documentation (the vendor survey forms) ranges from 2 to 75 pages. From these rather broad limits on desired information, you can realize why some quality control managers (particularly in small business firms) spend half their time answering questions and escorting customers or prospective customers through their facilities.

An **objective** individual or group from Quality, Purchasing, Engineering and Manufacturing should perform a **subjective** vendor and management evaluation survey. Major considerations governing survey participants should be cost, time, design or production schedules and specific requirements (quality, reliability, value engineering). A word of caution: In many cases, the number of people surveying a company is greater than the total labor force. This is ridiculous, embarrassing, costly and a complete waste of everyone's time and talents.

Surveys should be conducted under the cognizance of the independent quality control or quality assurance division of your company. The importance of having qualified professional personnel in this vital function of the quality organization cannot be overstressed. Surveyors must be talented and experienced in quality control, quality assurance, production control, industrial engineering and industrial management.

This requirement is especially important in smaller organizations that cannot assign specific personnel to conduct, for example, special process surveys, electronic vendor surveys and mechanical or machine shop vendor surveys.

The professional experience factor is of prime importance in order to allow an individual to assess effectively all areas within the assigned plant. The only way to obtain this knowledge, of course, is by work, training and experience. An important point to remember is that those conducting surveys represent your company and your management. Inexperienced or incapable personnel can project a poor company image to the vendor. In fact, the use of inexperienced personnel is a major cause of ineffective surveys.

When team effort is required, the professional quality representative should head the team and be the focal point for collecting all pertinent facts and recommendations from the other members. The quality representative should document all findings and factually rate the vendor in accordance with a planned quality capability rating system which covers appropriate areas of the survey.

Protect Your Investment

You are making an investment in a vendor every time you contract for a major purchase. The survey is a means of determining the soundness of your potential investments: can the vendor consistently produce a quality product, on time, at a price you are willing to pay. The "up-front" survey is a sound investment many times less the end cost of placing your order with an unacceptable or incapable vendor, especially when you take into account such factors as work stoppage, schedule slippage, scrap, rework, failures and customer reaction and dissatisfaction.

When individually done, vendor surveys are naturally more costly, since they involve labor, travel and living expenses.

Multiple surveys are cost effective: they produce maximum results for minimum cost. Thus, it pays to plan surveys by central areas. Some companies establish central survey headquarters in major areas of the country, reducing operating and travel costs. This type of arrangement also permits economical follow-up for source inspection and surveillance when required.

Typical Example

The following is typical of what can be accomplished by a planned program based on quality history compiled during a two-year period, the average cost per survey was approximately $67.00. This includes travel and living expenses and covers all sections of the country with all surveys conducted from the main plant. The figure does not include labor (salary), which will vary from company to company, and is confined to the vendor quality assurance department responsible for all surveys.

An Early Warning System typically results in:

1. Establishment of a level of confidence in the vendor's ability and capability before the fact.

2. Advance knowledge of the risk involved in placing the order with the vendor.

3. Time to work with the vendor on known deficiencies.

4. A factual documented evaluation of the vendor's quality system, management and associated factors.

5. Preplanning for source inspection and receiving inspection operations.

6. Receipt of sufficient information regarding the cost of vendor and/or subcontractor records for management evaluation, thus permitting sound "make or buy" decisions.

7. Assistance to purchasing, quality, engineering and manufacturing groups in meeting their obligations.

Approach your vendor and management evaluation surveys with a planned systematic program based on facts that have been documented and rated by qualified professional personnel and I am confident that you will find these surveys to be a practical and cost-effective Early Warning System.

Desirable Survey Information

1. Procedures—Q. C. operating procedures; inspection and test instructions; workmanship standards; compliance with procedures.

2. Control of purchases and vendors—Qualify vendor's parts prior to use? Maintain government or company QPL? Quality requirements on PO's? Vendor analysis? History records?

3. Drawing and change control—Responsibility? Latest in use? Changes to vendors? Company and government specifications available?

4. Inspection and test equipment—Scheduled calibrations? Traceable to NBS? All equipment identified and currently calibrated? Use of MIL-C-45662?

5. Material review; control of discrepant material—Maintain MRB? Material identified? Documented corrective action?

6. Receiving inspection; in-process and final inspection and test—Material identified? Use checklist/traveler? Raw material and special process certification available? Perform first-piece inspection? Inspection status? Inspection/test equipment adequate? Inspection areas adequate? Records retained?

7. Packing and shipping inspection—Instructions used? Verify final acceptance? Packaging tests conducted?

8. Stock control—Material readily identifiable? Traceable to PO if required? Facilities and space adequate? Stockroom open or closed? Stock rotation?

9. Environmental test facilities—Available? Documented test results? Equipment included in calibration system?

10. Housekeeping/material handling—Materials, supplies, and work arranged in neat manner? Clean? Maintained? Necessary clean-room facilities available?

11. Sampling inspection—Used? Where? Statistically valid? Records?

12. Process control—Chemical/physical test lab maintained? Systematic tests/analyses performed? Records? Applicable personnel and equipment certified/qualified?

13. Reliability/Value Engineering—Separate organizations? Evaluation of company products made? Documented reliability and value engineering policies and procedures? Failure analyses? Experience in reliability/value engineering? Field performance data available?

14. Special processes—Type? In-plant? Subcontract? Control?

15. General information—Have union? Contract date? Quality cost program? Government-approved purchasing department? Purchasing procedures in effect? Sales in dollars? Security regulations? Buildings? Growth-expansion plans? Names and tenure of company officers? Number and disposition of employes by organization? Major customers?

16. Any and all related comments and/or specific questions as appropriate to the company being evaluated.

Remember, the key to your Early Warning System is the professional vendor survey and product audit by qualified professional quality personnel.

VENDOR QUALITY AND MANAGEMENT

EVALUATION SURVEY FORM

Considerations for Use

This form may be used as a Personal Professional Evaluation as performed by a Professional Quality Engineer, Consultant or as a team effort with Purchasing, Engineering, Manufacturing and other qualified individuals. The final version of the form must be completed by the Quality Assurance Person in charge of the survey.

This form may also be used as a Pre-Survey Evaluation Form, in which case the form is mailed in total or an abbreviated short form version, to the vendor for him to complete and return to you for preliminary evaluation. The completed form shall be evaluated by the Vendor Quality Assurance Department. Evaluated copies shall be sent to Purchasing and to other concerned departments in order to determine if a Personal Professional Survey will be made. Perhaps the postage will be your only investment.

All survey forms shall be retained by the Vendor Quality Assurance Department after communication, coordination and joint evaluation with the Purchasing Department. The Vendor Quality Assurance Department shall assist the Purchasing Department in every way possible by providing Professional Surveys, evaluations and source inspections.

C. L. CARTER JR. & ASSOCIATES, INC.
VENDOR QUALITY & MANAGEMENT
EVALUATION SURVEY

Date: ______________ Survey No. ______________

( )		( )
Company Name	Telephone	President ( )
Address		V-Pres./Gen. Mgr. ( )
Div. of Subsidiary of		Chief Engineer ( )
Quality Cont. Mgr.	Reports to (title)	Asst. Q.C. Mgr.

Principal Product/ Process/Service	Government %		
	Commercial %		
No. of Employees____ Previous High____ Year	Major Customers:	Gov't.-Cust. Source Insp. yes no	Agency: Resident____ Itinerent
Elec. Inspection____ Mech. Inspection____ R & D - Eng.	Quality Control Manual: yes no / Date Last Review/ Revision:	Available for Review: yes no	Date Available:
Total Quality Control: Production: / Other: Ratio:	Appr.NASA____ MIL-Q-9858____ MIL-I-45208____ Other / Approving Agency:	Other Approvals:	List of Test Equip. Avail. yes____ no____ Date:
Reliability/V.E. Prog. Operational yes no	Define:	Trng. Program Operational: yes no	Type:

SURVEY RATING

Procedures____ Supplies/Vendors____ Dwg. & Change Control____ Insp. & Test Equip.____
Discrepant Mat'l. Control____ Rec. Insp.____ In Process Insp.____ Final Inspection____
Pack & Ship Insp.____, Stock Control____ Environ Test____ Housekeeping Mat'l.Handling____
Sample Inspection____ Process Control____ Rel.-Value Eng.____ Mgt/Organization____

Average____

Approved____ Cond'l.Approved____ Disapproved____

Quality Capability Rating:

0-1 Little or No System
1-2 System Inoperative/Ineffective
2-3 Major System Problems
3-4 Minor Problems to Acceptable

COMMENTS: ______________

Personnel Contacted: ______________

______________ Surveyed By: ______________

Note: Number in ( ) indicates years in business or time with company.

COMPANY NAME:____________________________

1. GENERAL INFORMATION

1. Have Union?___Name____________
   Contract date____________________
2. Have Quality Cost Program?____
   Mgt. Review?_____When?_________
3. Gov't. approved purchasing
   dept?_______Agency____________
4. Purch. procedures in effect?
   ____
5. Last year's gross sales_______
6. Financial statement available?
   ____
7. Security regulations required?
   Clearance level_______________
8. Number of buildings___________
   Condition_____________________
9. Growth & Expansion Plans?
   ____

2. PROCEDURES

Y N

__ __ ___ 1. Maintain written Quality Control Procedures?
__ __ ___ 2. Maintain inspection & Test instructions?
__ __ ___ 3. Maintain workmanship standards?
__ __ ___ 4. Compliance to established procedures, standards, etc?

______ Total Average_________

3. CONTROL OF SUPPLIES & VENDORS

Y N

__ __ ___ 1. Qualify suppliers parts prior to use?
__ __ ___ 2. Maintain qualified products list, (Gov't.and/or company)?
__ __ ___ 3. Review suppliers Quality Control System, Documented?
__ __ ___ 4. Quality requirements included in purchase documents (certification, test reports, quality system, etc?)
__ __ ___ 5. Purchase document review or audit?
__ __ ___ 6. Maintain vendor analysis/rating program?
__ __ ___ 7. Are vendor history records used in making procurement decisions?

______ Total Average_________

4. DRAWING AND CHANGE CONTROL

Y N

__ __ ___ 1. Specific responsibility for drawing and change control, ___Q.C., ___Eng., ___Prod.?
__ __ ___ 2. Dwg/Spec. location records maintained?
__ __ ___ 3. Latest drawings/specification in use?
__ __ ___ 4. Q. C. responsible for change effectivity verification?
__ __ ___ 5. Program for processing changes to suppliers?
__ __ ___ 6. Customers notified of significant proprietary changes?
__ __ ___ 7. Applicable company specs available?
__ __ ___ 8. Applicable customer specs available?

______ Total Average_________

5. INSPECTION AND TEST EQUIPMENT

Y N

__ __ ___ 1. Scheduled electrical/mechanical calibrations?
__ __ ___ 2. Effective recall system?
__ __ ___ 3. Standards traceable to NBS?
   Through_______________________
__ __ ___ 4. All equipment identified and currently calibrated?
__ __ ___ 5. Tooling used for acceptance included in calibration system?
__ __ ___ 6. Employee owned acceptance tools controlled?
__ __ ___ 7. Primary stds. isolated to prevent unauthorized usage?
__ __ ___ 8. Primary power for final test monitored with variation compensation?

______ Total Average_________

6. MATERIAL REVIEW, CONTROL OF DISCREPANT MATERIAL

Y N

__ __ ___ 1. Maintain MRB? Members:
   ____
__ __ ___ 2. Discrepant material physically identified? How?__________
__ __ ___ 3. Discrepant material removed from production flow?
__ __ ___ 4. Maintain records of all MRB action?
__ __ ___ 5. Documented corrective action system?

______ Total Average_________

COMPANY NAME: ____________________

7. RECEIVING INSPECTION

Y N

___ ___ ___ 1. Material identified and segregated to preclude unauthorized usage?
___ ___ ___ 2. Use inspection checklists?
___ ___ ___ 3. Insp./Test equipment adequate?
___ ___ ___ 4. Maintain vendor history records?
___ ___ ___ 5. Drawings/specs/PO's available?
___ ___ ___ 6. Raw material & special process certifications available?
___ ___ ___ 7. Scheduled certification verification?

______ Total Average__________

8. IN-PROCESS INSPECTION/TEST

Y N

___ ___ ___ 1. Perform first article insp.?
___ ___ ___ 2. Performed or verified by Q.C.?
___ ___ ___ 3. Instructions/checklists used?
___ ___ ___ 4. Results recorded on units travelers or other identifying documents?
___ ___ ___ 5. Inspection status readily evident?
___ ___ ___ 6. Inspection/test equip. adequate?
___ ___ ___ 7. Inspection areas adequate?

______ Total Average__________

9. FINAL INSPECTION/TEST

Y N

___ ___ ___ 1. Performed or witnessed by Q.C.?
___ ___ ___ 2. Results recorded on units, travelers, or other identifying documents?
___ ___ ___ 3. Records retained?
___ ___ ___ 4. Instructions/checklists used?
___ ___ ___ 5. Inspection/test equip. adequate?
___ ___ ___ 6. Inspection areas adequate?

______ Total Average__________

10. PACKING AND SHIPPING INSPECTION

Y N

___ ___ ___ 1. Instructions/checklist used?
___ ___ ___ 2. System to verify final acceptance?
___ ___ ___ 3. System to safeguard quality between final acceptance and shipping?
___ ___ ___ 4. Packaging test conducted, when required?

______ Total Average__________

11. STOCK CONTROL

Y N

___ ___ ___ 1. Stock readily identified?
___ ___ ___ 2. Material traceable to receiving insp. records?
___ ___ ___ 3. Facilities & space adequate? Stockroom: Open___ Closed______
___ ___ ___ 4. Stock rotation plan (first in - first out).

______ Total Average__________

12. ENVIRONMENTAL TEST FACILITIES

Y N

___ ___ ___ 1. Facilities available? Types:
____
____
___ ___ ___ 2. Test result documentation available?
___ ___ ___ 3. Equipment included in calibration system?
___ ___ ___ 4. All equip. identified, currently calibrated & maint.?

______ Total Average__________

13. HOUSEKEEPING/MAT'L. HANDLING/ FACILITIES

Y N

___ ___ ___ 1. Materials, supplies & work arranged in neat manner?
___ ___ ___ 2. Work & storage areas clean and maintained?
___ ___ ___ 3. Clean room facilities? Level:
____
___ ___ ___ 4. Procedures for maintenance?
___ ___ ___ 5. General appearance & condition
____

______ Total Average__________

14. SAMPLE INSPECTION

Y N

___ ___ ___ 1. Sample plan used? Describe:
____
Where: ____________________
______Receiving ______In-Process ______Final
___ ___ ___ 2. Statistically valid?
___ ___ ___ 3. Sampling schedules posted in inspection areas?
___ ___ ___ 4. Appropriate records available?

______ Total Average__________

COMPANY NAME: ____________________

15. PROCESS CONTROL

Y N

___ ___ ___ 1. Maintain chemical/physical test lab?

___ ___ ___ 2. Systematic tests/analysis performed?

___ ___ ___ 3. Records of tests/analysis results available?

___ ___ ___ 4. Applicable personnel and equipment certified/qualified; i.e., soldering, welding, etc.

___ Total Average ____

16. RELIABILITY/VALUE ENG.

Y N

___ ___ ___ 1. Separate Rel. Organization?

___ ___ ___ 2. Separate V.E. Organization?

___ ___ ___ 3. Evaluation of Co. Products Made?
By Whom? ____
When? ___ All? ___ By Contract?
____

___ ___ ___ 4. Documented Rel. & V.E. policies and procedures?

___ ___ ___ 5. Failure Analysis Conducted?
By Whom? ____

___ ___ ___ 6. Experience in Rel/V.E.?

___ ___ ___ 7. Field Performance Data Avail.?
How obtained? ____

___ Total Average ____

SPECIAL PROCESS

PROCESS	IN PLANT	SUB CONT.	CONTROL	SUBCONTRACTOR	
Heat Treat	___	___	___	___	___
Plating (Type)	___	___	___	___	___
Chem, Film (Type)	___	___	___	___	___
Painting	___	___	___	___	___
Ultrasonic Clean	___	___	___	___	___
X-ray, Zyglo, Magnflux	___	___	___	___	___
Welding (Type)	___	___	___	___	___
Soldering (Type)	___	___	___	___	___
Printing-Screening	___	___	___	___	___
Printed Circuits	___	___	___	___	___
Others	___	___	___	___	___
___	___	___	___	___	___
___	___	___	___	___	___

ADDITIONAL COMMENTS: ____________________

C. L. Carter Jr. & Associates, Inc.

REQUEST FOR VENDOR SURVEY

_____ CRITICAL _____ MAJOR _____ MINOR

____
Vendor's Name and Address

Persons to Be Contacted: ______________________________

Product: ______________________________

Requested By: ______________________________ Date __________

Company Name and Department

Required Date of Completion: ______________________________

Contract or Program: ______________________________

Comments: ______________________________

____

____

____

Scheduled Date: ______________________________

Coordinator: ______________________________

Survey By: ______________________________

Transportation _____ Air _____ Local

Costs—Single Survey: ______________________________

Costs—Multiple Survey: ______________________________

Survey Number: ______________________________

CRITICAL—No previous survey, high dollar on contract, little or no history, requires MIL-Q-9858, high reliability required, critical problems, etc.

MAJOR—Previous survey inadequate, high dollar, high volume, limited history, proposed vendor, major problems, audit.

MINOR—Previous survey adequate, medium dollar, medium volume, additional source, proposed vendor, minor problems, surveillance.

QUALITY SURVEY SOURCES

A group of aerospace corporations have, for the past few years, coordinated their vendor survey information on acceptable quality vendors. They call their efforts "Coordinated Aerospace Supplier Evaluation" or C.A.S.E.

Each of the C.A.S.E. corporations deposit copies of their approved quality evaluated sources into a centralized computer, which is under the direction of one of the aerospace firms. The quality-approved vendors are then placed in "The C.A.S.E. Register", which gives the vendor's name, address, etc.; quality system approval level, i.e., MIL-Q-9858, MIL-I-45208, NASA 200-3, etc.; the survey date; and the special process or capability of the vendor.

The purpose and intent of the coordinated effort is to reduce survey costs and to reduce the number of surveys conducted by the corporations against the same vendors. This certainly makes a lot of sense and is very helpful to the small vendor, who is subject to being surveyed by hundreds of major firms.

The C.A.S.E. Register then becomes one of the prime sources for thousands of theoretically qualified vendors. In short, the C.A.S.E. Register contains vendors who have been surveyed and found to be 'acceptable by quality' by one or more of the major aerospace corporations. No one guarantees anything, but the Register is a real starting point for quality vendors. The C.A.S.E. Register can be purchased.

The Vendor-Vendee Technical Committee of the American Society for Quality Control is investigating and evaluating a professional qualification of quality-approved vendors. Surveys would only be performed by trained, qualified, professional quality engineers. The list or book of quality-approved vendors would probably be provided to business, industry, and government agencies for a pre-arranged fee.

Qualified quality consultants, listed in the A.S.Q.C. Quality Progress Magazine, provide another source of professional vendor quality surveys, surveillance, or special evaluations as may be necessary by project, program or research and development studies.

VENDOR RATING

I would like to briefly cover Vendor Rating as another area which has had many, many ups and downs during the past few years.

Vendor Ratings are generally not accepted, because they are not understood by Purchasing, the Vendor, and in many cases, by the people who have generated the Hocus Pocus Numbers Game of many Vendor Ratings. Fancy formulas and exotic misunderstood statistical applications have done nothing to increase Purchasing's confidence in Quality Control techniques, because they are not able to understand what they are reading. We must stay very basic for clear communication, coordination, and unlimited cooperation.

Purchasing wants facts and figures from which decisions can be made. They want to analyze trends and discuss problem areas with their vendors. However, their vendors must also understand, or communication will be a major problem.

I recommend that all Vendor Rating be accomplished in the Universal Language that everyone understands—Dollars and Cents.

This is illustrated as follows: Purchasing agrees to pay $2.00 for an item, which includes receiving the item; conducting a normal sample inspection; accepting the item; sending it to stock; and, processing the paperwork for payment. That's what you agreed to, and that's what you should get. If the item is Rejected for "out of tolerance conditions as caused by the Vendors," then you have at that point, "added cost to the item." Additional samples may be needed; a rejection report must be written; the item must be segregated and possibly sent to a Material Review Board for action. All of this causes considerable costs to be added to the item which can be determined to be another 50c per item. Standard costs can be utilized for ease of operation and understanding by Purchasing, the Vendor, and Company Management.

The Vendor Rating can reflect Price, Delivery, and Quality as rated and reported in dollars and cents for unified understanding, which will result in much better Communication, Coordination, and Cooperation.

The cost effective use of computers for many phases of Engineering, Purchasing, Manufacturing, Production, and Inventory Control, Quality Control and Quality Assurance, Calibration and Accounting are in full swing today. Vendor Ratings compiled from Vendor History Data as retrieved from the computer is a good technique being widely used in the larger corporations. This technique can be used by the smaller companies as time and talent will allow. The small company with limited numbers of vendors can achieve good results by utilizing receiving inspection records as compiled in dollars and cents consistent with your company operation. The key is "simplicity."

Many of the larger corporations run "Tab Runs" from the computer which are reviewed with "out of control Vendors" for timely, corrective action and for awareness by all concerned individuals or other corporate divisions using the same vendor. The computer can be called a major piece of Quality Information Equipment. Unfortunately, the Quality Organizations are sometimes the last ones to go "on the computer" or allowed to have "Computer Time" to obtain Quality data. Wise Management will put Quality Up-Front on the computer and everywhere else for Quality, Value, and Integrity.

Incentive Systems for Vendors are coming on strong and paying good dividends for both the Vendor and Vendee. Some companies utilize the Motivational Program Technique in much the same way they utilize this internally within the company. I favor the incentive approach which objectively recognizes the outstanding Vendor for outstanding Performance in Price, Delivery, and Quality. Incentive awards can be plaques, trophies, certificates, or monetary remuneration.

The small, medium, and large company must be considered on an equal basis. The Small Precision Vendor can often be worth as much if not more than the giant corporation. You can rate them on an equal basis by using the dollars and cents approach for obtaining Quality, Value, and Integrity from your Vendors.

I have included a simple dollars and cents rating program for your information in establishing a system as appropriate to your needs. Remember, keep it simple, understandable, and functional. This effort on your part will save money and provide purchasing with factual data which will allow them to make timely management decisions relative to seeking new vendors, second sources of supply, discussing problems with vendors or praising vendors for outstanding performance.

"How to Control Vendor Quality in Dollars and Cents" is a simple Vendor Rating System which can be used to factually Rate, Charge, or Cost out REJECTIONS FOR CAUSE. This is an excellent motivating tool for Management, Purchasing, and the Vendor. You will note that the most expensive item of Rejection Cost is the one as titled Customer Rejected Material. Even the dollars as stated cannot reflect the total cost of Customer Dissatisfaction. You may never know what the cost is in Lost Business, Reduced Sales, and many other intangibles.

"HOW TO CONTROL VENDOR QUALITY" . . .

DOLLARS AND CENTS

Item Cost: $100.00

Criteria: Normal Inspection; Accept to Stated AQL; To Stock; Pay Vendor

Rejection Costs: **Charge to OUR COMPANY** for Cause as based on Drawing Errors; Engineering Problems; Production Control and/or Purchasing Problems . . .

Charge to VENDOR for Cause as based on Out of Spec.; Wrong Parts; Wrong Quantity; Poor Workmanship as defined by Standards; Damage based on Packaging and/or Poor Handling . . .

Customer Rejected Material: **$25.00** Note: Add other items accordingly

Rejection Report:	$5.00	
Material Review:	$5.00	
More Samples:	$1.00	each
Rework to Spec.:	$1.00	each . . . other costs as appropriate
Return to Vendor:	$5.00	
Use as is:	$ .50	each
Wrong Parts (All)	$5.00	
Wrong Parts (Par.)	$2.50	
Wrong Qty. (over)	$ .50	each
Wrong Qty. (under)	$2.50	each
Damaged Parts:	$2.50	each
Dwg. Error: Major	$5.00	
Minor	$2.50	
Eng. Prob.: Major	$5.00	
Minor	$2.50	
Prod. Cont. Qty.:	$5.00	
Purch. Ord. Prob.	$5.00	
Q.C. Errors	$5.00	
Delivery N.O.S.	$5.00	Charge to Company or Vendor for Cause
Price Per Item:	$5.00	To be determined by Purchasing
	$3.00	To be determined by Purchasing
	$1.00	To be determined by Purchasing
Complexity Factor:	$1.00	Very Complex: Determined by Q.C. & Eng.
	$2.00	Complex: Determined by Q.C. & Eng.
	$3.00	Simple Part: Determined by Q.C. & Eng.

Add respective costs to cost of item as necessary. Total for Rating.

Key: Vendor ABC .... Total Cost: $100.00 Agreed Cost: $100.00 Rating: 1.00

Key: Vendor XYZ .... Total Cost: $200.00 Agreed Cost: $100.00 Rating: 2.00

Key: Vendor PDQ .... Total Cost: $ 50.00 Agreed Cost: $ 50.00 Rating: 1.00

Scale: To be set as based on Business/Industry:

1.00 Excellent
1.15 Good
1.25 Acceptable
1.40 Marginal
1.50 Poor
1.65 Unacceptable

The Vendor & Vendee Both Understand Dollars & Cents . . .

THINGS TO REMEMBER ABOUT VENDOR QUALITY ASSURANCE

1. V.Q.A. is a support function to and for Purchasing.
2. Purchasing is responsible for the procurement of everything for the company, from qualified vendors, at the lowest total cost, on time, and of acceptable quality to stated standards.
3. V.Q.A. is to assist Purchasing.
4. V.Q.A. should not dictate who to buy from. Recommend—yes; Dictate—no!
5. Typical reasons for V.Q.A. to survey the capability of vendors include:
   A. New supplier; critical or "high dollar" parts; special processes;
   B. Quality history indicates survey is needed; problem vendor;
   C. Weak vendor; poor price and delivery; change in location or ownership.
6. All surveys must be arranged through Purchasing for good communication, coordination, and cooperation.
7. As an organization of professionals, the A.S.Q.C. should take the lead in establishing functional, practical, attainable standards for Vendor Quality Assurance Surveys and related activities. The ASQC should provide professional quality standards for business, industry, and government, when necessary or requested.
8. An 'Up-Front' Vendor Quality Assurance effort by professional quality people can be your cost effective early warning system.
9. Qualified vendors are a major asset to any organization, be it com-

mercial, industrial, or governmental. Everyone in Purchasing and Quality should work together as a team to Obtain, Qualify and Retain, Qualified Vendors.

10. Whenever you evaluate the vendor, be sure to audit and evaluate his as built, as currently produced product. This will give you an Up-Front look at what you will probably be getting if you decide to do business with him. Take corrective action early. Insist on and receive Quality Products from the start.
11. Communicate, coordinate and cooperate with Purchasing for Quality, Value and Integrity for your company.
12. Purchasing wants facts and figures from which decisions can be made. They want to analyze trends and discuss problems with the vendors. Quality must Rate the Vendors in the Universal understandable language of Dollars and Cents. The Vendor Rating must be a combined, coordinated effort by Quality and Purchasing. In this way the Vendor will become a working part of the total quality team because the vendor can understand his rating when presented in simple terms of dollars and cents.

Chapter 11

VALUE ANALYSIS AND COST REDUCTION

In reviewing the definition for Value Analysis, I believe you can see that we can Value Analyze practically anything, including the Sugar Dispenser and Napkin Holder in every restaurant; complex Electro-Mechanical Systems; Electronic Equipment; specific Components; documented Systems & Procedures, Specifications, and many other items of interest to you and your organization.

The theory, application and techniques remain basically constant, regardless of the item or system to be Value Analyzed. We will review some of the basic elements, but first I would like to discuss the term 'Value'.

Value is a variable. The value of a cup of cool water to a thirsty person varies with the distance from a source of drinking water. The value of a radio or computer to an astronaut in flight is vastly different from its value to my son or daughter. The logic of these examples illustrates that Value is a variable.

Value, although a broad term, has been specifically categorized so that it can be defined with meaning.

USE VALUE is based on the properties and qualities of a product, material or system which accomplishes a use, work or service.

COST VALUE is based on the cost of a product or service, and is almost always expressed in money.

ESTEEM VALUE is based on the properties, features or attractiveness involved in the pride of ownership.

EXCHANGE VALUE is based on the properties or qualities which make the product exchangeable or tradeable for something else.

For the vast majority of items, Use Value and Cost Value are virtually the only factors of significance. These can be stated in precise terms. Use Value can be stated in terms of Operating Requirements or Functional Characteristics. Cost Value, in terms of dollars and cents. Since they are generally precise and measurable, they can be dealt with on an objective basis.

For the purpose of review as related to all of the above: Value Analysis is an organized effort directed at analyzing the function of an item, system or service with the purpose of achieving the required function at the lowest over-all cost.

There are Seven Basic Elements associated with Value Analysis.

They are not always distinct and separate for, in practice, they often merge or overlap. The elements are:

1. **Item Selection:** The selection of the item or system to which Value Analysis efforts are to be applied.
2. **Determination of Function:** The analysis and definition of function(s) that must be performed by the item or system.
3. **Gathering Information:** Obtaining all pertinent facts concerning the item or system; the present cost, quality and reliability requirements, historical facts, etc.
4. **Developing Alternatives:** The creation of ideas for alternatives.
5. **Cost Analysis of Alternatives:** The development of cost estimates of alternatives, and the selection of one or more of the more economical ones for further evaluation and analysis of technical or practical feasibility.
6. **Testing and Verification:** Proof that the alternative(s) will not jeopardize fulfillment of performance, functional, and/or appearance requirements.
7. **Proposal Submission and Follow-up:** Preparation and submission of a formal Value Analysis Change Proposal. The Action Phase.

Another means of describing the substance of the Seven Elements is to point out that doing them provides answers to the following questions.

1. What is it?
2. What does it do?
3. What does it cost?
4. What is it worth?
5. What else might do the job?
6. What do they cost?
7. Which is the least expensive?
8. Will it meet the requirements?
9. What is needed to implement?

Value Analysis is a technique for making decisions. It is an organized effort to identify, remove and/or reduce unnecessary costs, and a tool for Business and Industrial Management. However, Value Analysis is meaningless until it is put to work and is producing cost reducing results. This can be accomplished by instituting a Value Analysis Program. The Program can be made an integral part of the Total Quality Assurance Program.

There are basic elements needed to implement a Value Analysis

Program, although the quantity of each element will vary with the size of the Business or Industrial organization. The Key Elements include:

1. A Value Analysis Consultant, Analyst or Staff to conduct the Indoctrination, Orientation and Training; to develop specific Value Analysis techniques, research, standards and data as appropriate to the company; to provide guidance, direction and technical assistance, and conduct Value Analysis studies, audits and special assignments; to stimulate, motivate and provide incentives for creativity and teamwork.

2. Indoctrination and orientation for Management and Personnel in the concepts, objectives and techniques associated with the Value Analysis Program. This is done to provide understanding, and gain management support and endorsement of the Program.

3. Specific Training in Value Analysis techniques for all Key Management Personnel. This will enable them to contribute to the Value Analysis effort, and motivate them to meet cost targets and cost reduction goals.

4. A Cost Target Program to provide motivation for Management and Personnel to meet cost objectives; to measure cost effectiveness, and provide the force for the application of Value Analysis techniques throughout the company.

I can safely say that any company can benefit from having a Value Analysis Program, regardless of its size. This is particularly true if a product or service is being sold on the competitive market, and if Management wants increased profits and reduced costs.

The basic, key factor in setting up a Value Analysis Program is obtaining professional Value Analysis knowledge, skill and personnel. It has been proven that success of the Program is based on having the services of a Value Analysis specialist. He should be a creative individual, a motivator, an analyst and counselor. He should comprehend technical problems, and have knowledge of processes, procedures, systems, materials, product, vendors, and a general understanding of the business functions connected with the company. I would suggest that the individual be the Program Manager within the Quality Assurance Organization of small and medium sized companies, so that he can serve all functions of the business, and provide assistance to the General Management and Personnel in achieving Value Improvement and Cost Reductions.

An effective Value Analysis Program will assure maximum value and reduced costs, while maintaining the required function, acceptable levels of Quality and Reliability, and Product Integrity.

Management should periodically review the return on investment to assure that the Program is producing actual, tangible results. An initial goal of 5 to 1 Savings to Program Costs ratio, should be achieved with proficiency.

To restate an old cliche, "Quality, Value and Integrity Pays Dividends to Management and Personnel who put their dollars 'Up Front' in the Planning, Engineering, Analysis and Prevention Stages, for Cost Reductions, Product, Production and Profit Improvements."

The **"Ten Commandments of Cost Reduction"** (as extracted from Phil Carroll's in Factory Magazine), are presented as appropriate guidelines for Management and Personnel in every Business, Industry, Educational or Governmental organization.

1. Thou shalt make known to all thy people whence cometh their provider and that their paper shuffling will profit them nothing unless the customers get their orders in good time ...
2. Thou shalt not enter into a new land nor bring forth a new product until thou hast clearly set down forecasts of the goods that the hosts desire ...
3. Thou shalt handeth no coins to those of thy peddlers who either maketh long journeys to sip wine with customers that ringeth up only small accounts or who offereth strange and curious departures from the product line ...
4. Thou shalt settle upon and inscribe on blue paper exactly what workmen are to make, and how, so their pieces fitteth together one with another and with those sent into far lands ...
5. Thou shalt plan all work, both for the multitude and for their leaders, so that neither people nor equipment nor goods shall wait; causing losses to thy firm and disappointment to thy customers ...
6. Thou shalt reward the uncommon among thy people who bring in much harvest or cometh forth with better ways or turneth out extra pieces ...
7. Thou shalt not worship the methods nor designs nor layouts you use, for verily there are better ways and thou must seek them out so that thy enterprise may survive ...
8. Thou shalt not suffer anyone to spoil nor to waste nor to steal the materials thou buyest—for all these shall enter into the

goods to be exchanged for gold in the market place ...

9. Thou shalt not prepare multitudes of scrolls for trifling amounts nor waste thy substance for covetous purposes nor for graven images of thy leaders, for each coin used shall bring forth still another and not beget dross ...
10. Thou shalt be at pains to learn quickly of conduct that meeteth not thy goals, and take prompt action to restore thy good works so thy people may prosper ...

I would suggest that you review these Ten Commandments from time to time, and Value Analyze their worth to the operation of your organization for achieving and maintaining Quality, Value, and Integrity.

Cost Effectiveness and Cost Reduction should be of prime interest to all Management and Personnel in every organization for cost savings can result in increased profit, increased earnings, greater growth, development, and personal satisfaction.

There are many areas where we can reduce costs or suggest that cost reduction studies be conducted. These would include:

1. Personnel Recruiting and Hiring Practices. An example would be where companies advertise for personnel (half or full-page ads) but do not have the jobs. They are advertising to maintain their "Image" as being a growth company while in reality they are in a downward trend and laying off personnel. Another example is indiscriminate Hire in the front door and Fire others out the back door. This will catch up to the company in due time and create a very poor image which will be very hard to overcome. It does not take long for the word to get around about Hire and Fire personnel practices. I know of a major corporation that was still trying to change that image 10 years later after 1 year of Unstable Personnel Hiring and Firing practices.

   Another good example is high personnel turnover which can be attributed to many, many things. Some of these include: inexperienced unqualified personnel departments, no organization structure; employees have no confidence in personnel department; excessively long time in processing personnel changes and payroll increases; (Note: This will substantially increase turnover and should be checked before it gets out of hand.)

personnel department has no authority; personnel department does not know how to recruit, nor how to interview.

2. Government Paper work and duplication of effort is a very sore subject with many people. It has often been said that, "The Government paper work and red tape associated with obtaining, producing, delivering, and receiving payment for an item would create a pile of paper that was taller than and weighed more than the item being purchased."

Although I'm sure this is true in many, many cases, I must also point out the inefficiency connected with having to send 10 copies of progress reports to people who are retaining redundant records just for the sake of having records. This might be called "creating a duplication of effort" or "creating a job to build an empire." Both of these are very costly to everyone concerned, with particular emphasis placed on cost to the taxpayer, cost to the company, cost to the person in terms of job satisfaction, and cost to the customer.

3. Every department in every company is prime and fertile ground for cost reduction, value analysis, and quality assurance problems. I am sure you can quickly pick out some prime targets to evaluate and analyze. Just try this as a quick study:
   1. Conduct your own brainstorming session by writing down 5 or 10 specifics which come to your mind in which you feel cost reductions or improvements can be made. Examples: Paper work, forms, parts, products, processes, tools, etc.
   2. Evaluate and analyze your items.
   3. Pick out the one that has the greatest potential.
   4. Apply the seven basic elements as previously discussed.
   5. React with planned action and follow through.

You will be amazed with the results. Continue on with your second and third items. Try this technique at home. You can also save dollars with value analysis and cost reduction projects in the home.

Be aware of being cost effective at all times, at home and at work. You, your family, and your employer will benefit when you value analyze for cost effectiveness and cost reduction.

QUALITY COSTS, INVESTMENT AND RETURN

Quality costs as described in the understandable management language of Dollars and Cents are a vital part of the control and assurance of quality in any business. Quality costs as defined by four basic areas will appeal to progressive management and will be used by profit motivated management to reduce total costs. The four areas of quality costs include the following:

1. PREVENTION—Costs concerned with people and equipment working together designing, implementing and maintaining the total 'Before The Fact' Quality Assurance Program. The prevention of defective products in the fullest sense of the word. Prevent scrap, rework, and customer complaints. Audit the Program for 'Up-Front Prevention'.
2. DETECTION/APPRAISAL—Costs concerned with people and equipment measuring, inspecting, testing, evaluating and or auditing products, parts, components and all purchased items to determine conformance to quality standards and performance requirements. Detect substandard quality at any phase of the operation with examples being: source inspection; receiving inspection; in-process and final inspection, including product audits at any phase of the manufacturing cycle.
3. INTERNAL FAILURES—Costs created by defective parts, products, processes, procedures, components, materials and other items that fail to meet quality standards, drawings or specifications.
4. EXTERNAL FAILURES—Costs created by defective products as delivered to customers. Field failures and associated problems which cause customer dissatisfaction and loss of business.

Management must make an investment in Prevention and Detection/Appraisal to obtain reduced costs in Internal and External Failures. This investment will also reduce management's liability in the areas of Safety, Service and Product Integrity.

A B C—Simplicity

Quality Cost Data allows management to ANALYZE performance.
Quality Cost Data allows management to BUDGET objectively.
Quality Cost Data allows management to CONTROL projects, products and people.

Return on Investment

Management will be interested in their return on investment which experience indicates to be approximately 2 to 1 for some, 5 to 1 for others and up to or more than 10 to 1 for many firms. However, management must realize their return will not come overnight. There will be immediate, short and long term returns on quality investments and good management should be prepared to accept the planned long term benefits which are sure to come.

Professional quality people will not preach nor predict overnight quality success to management. In most cases, the quality problems did not happen overnight and they will not be corrected overnight. Quality cost data will provide management with positive profit potential. Quality can increase profits. Progressive management should and will have Professional Quality Advisors to assist executives in making Quality Decisions for short and long range cost reductions and for positive profit improvements.

The Quality Cost Committee of the American Society for Quality Control has done an outstanding job in their publication "Quality Costs —What and How" which I recommend for your information and use. I also recommend the ASQC Course as titled "Management of Quality Costs".

Please remember, an effective Quality Cost Program will allow you to quickly identify, evaluate, analyze and report Quality Costs and take prompt corrective action. The Total Quality Program will allow the company controllers and the quality controllers to communicate, coordinate and cooperate to reduce costs and increase profits. Start your Total Quality Program now and save more with cost effective Prevention.

Chapter 12

MANUFACTURING

Manufacturing can't build a quality product if engineering hasn't designed the proper quality into the product. Unified Quality Assurance Workmanship Standards are mandatory for the design, manufacture and purchase of quality products.

Manufacturing is responsible for the quality of the product they produce after they have accepted the quality of the released design from Engineering. Machine and process capability studies must be made before you can really establish attainable controls.

This doesn't sound too complicated, but I can assure you that the manufacturing operation is often the scene of Engineering Chaos! This is particularly true in job shop, small lot production, and highly technical products.

It seems that the product never quite makes it out of the engineering phase, and in many cases, the product goes to the customer in an unfinished state of engineering and manufacturing confusion. This can be illustrated by many, many cases of no one in the company knowing the configuration of the product they had shipped to the customer! This happens daily. As an example: Thirty-four changes or modifications were made to a product in the course of the manufacturing cycle. If no one kept records on what change was made on each unit, it would take a physical inventory of each unit, prior to shipment, to see and know what you were sending to the customer. If engineering change orders were not written for each change as made by manufacturing, there would be no control of design, not to mention a complete lack of control in manufacturing.

Engineering must control their design. Manufacturing must control their product. Manufacturing Quality Control in the larger companies is an integral part of the manufacturing organization, and operates as a member of the Total Quality Assurance Team in producing Quality products on time at the lowest cost.

Someone might say, "How can this non-controlled situation exist?" It's rather simple. If the design is not firm; if the product does not operate or function as required; if management and personnel don't care; if the customer is screaming for his past due product—then the product is subject to being shipped in most any category of configuration. As I said, it happens daily, and if you look at some of the Commercial, Industrial and Military products today, you can see what I mean.

The Manufacturing Organization should consist of qualified, trained production personnel and professional managerial and technical management and personnel at all levels.

The Manufacturing Organization will usually consist of Metal Fabrication, Machine Shop, Assembly Areas, Inspection, Test, and Shipping Functions, as complemented by Receiving, Stock, Production Control, Manufacturing Engineering, and associated necessary functions depending on the organization.

Manufacturing Quality Control will provide all Inspection and Test functions; generate plans and procedures for adequate control of in-line processes; provide process capability studies; establish Acceptable Quality Levels in all areas of Manufacturing as appropriate to the product or process, and in accordance with the Quality Assurance Management Policy and Program. Control Charts and records are set up and maintained at each operator's position, machine and/or processing station. Over-all Production, Delivery and Quality Performance Charts should be maintained in strategic areas for visual review and motivation.

In the smaller organization, the Quality function may be a separate line or staff organization. However, I firmly believe that Manufacturing is Responsible, and that Quality should not be a crutch for anyone. The attitude of 'sneak it by Quality' should be eliminated by Management. Place responsibility where it truly lies ... with the Management and Personnel who manufacture the product. If it's not right, they can blame no one but themselves.

Someone may say, "But if you hold Management responsible for Quality, they will ship defective products." Well, you must understand that we are talking about the **Personal Integrity of the Manufacturing Management and Personnel.** Executive Management's theme of operation must be Quality, Value and Integrity of Personnel, Products and Services. If Executive Management doesn't have confidence in their Management and Personnel, then they had better find some new people.

The Manufacturing and Quality functions go hand-in-hand. They provide products and services. They come in constant contact with the customers, and must satisfy Sales, Marketing and Engineering.

This truly requires a unified effort by the whole team. This truly requires Unified Quality Assurance Workmanship Standards for use in Engineering, Purchasing, Manufacturing and Quality. This truly requires controlled specifications, associated work instructions, process controls and procedures. This truly requires an enlightened Management and Personnel Team who understands and maintains Quality, Value and Integrity.

A Typical Process Control Chart is provided for your information and use. It is not my intent to duplicate the work of the many authors and books as referenced in chapter 3. Please refer to these for additional information on control charts.

Remember, Quality and Manufacturing along with Engineering and Purchasing, plus the support functions of Personnel, Sales and Accounting make up the Total Quality Team. Quality must be built in by everyone along the line from start to Finish.

TYPICAL PROCESS CONTROL CHART

A typical process control chart you can use to plot any given dimension with stated tolerances. Measurements should be taken on schedule by Quality Control Inspectors.

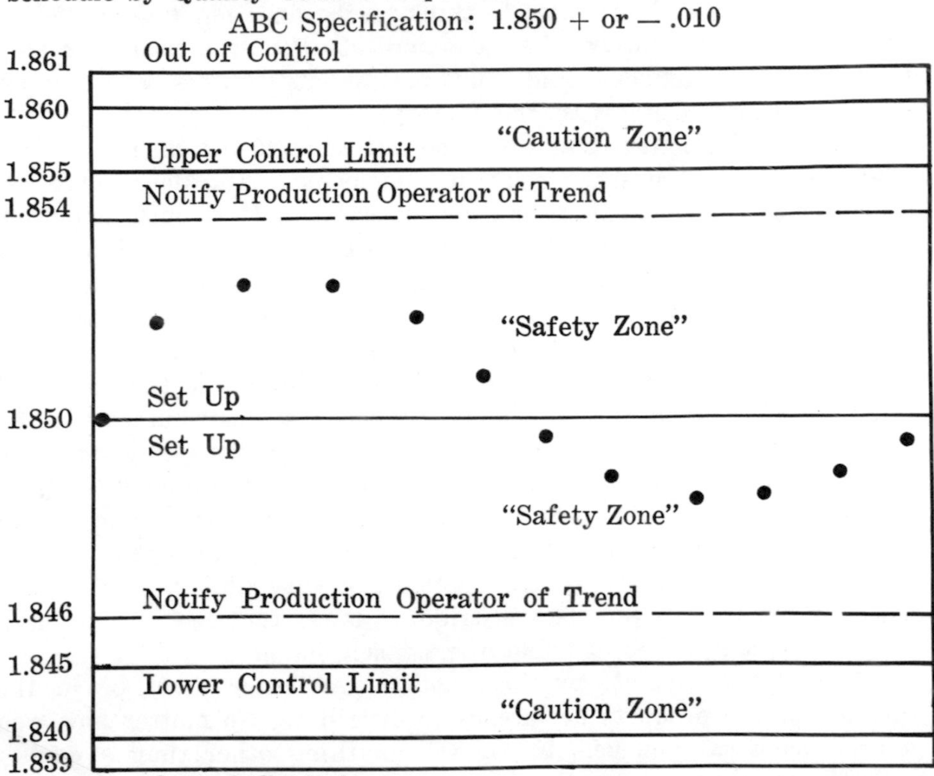

Out of Control

Example: Always set up the machine or process as close to actual 1.850 in order to utilize all of the given tolerance and stay within the upper and lower control safety limits. Report trends immediately to the production operator and to supervision. Always Stay Within the 1.840 and 1.860 for Actual Control. Remember, if you set up the machine or process at the upper or lower control limit you will be in trouble before you start because you have used your tolerances one way or the other against yourself and not to your benefit. Each Dot On The Chart Defines Actual Measurement Made Every 15 Minutes By The Quality Control Inspector.

Chapter 13

QUALITY DISTRIBUTORS

An ever increasing number of original equipment manufacturers and industrial users have come to think of the distributor as a useless middleman. Unfortunately, the facts indicate that the basis for this attitude is well founded and that useless distributors are forcing buyers to deal directly with the factory.

The distributor can blame no one but himself for having a poor reputation and, more specifically, management in the distributor organization is the real villain and major problem. It is quite apparent that distributor management has forgotten what services they must perform to justify their existence and also forgotten, if they ever understood, the meaning of P.D.Q. No matter what angle you use, Price, Delivery, and Quality, whether computed by hand, or by the latest computing machine, add up to Service. Service is the only real thing the distributor has to sell. This means the distributor must be more than a mere parts broker, more than just a dislocated warehouse, and more than a convenient single source for several commodities just to lighten purchasing's load. The distributor must be a much more complex animal, capable of a multitude of services and operated in a manner which will instill in the customer a very high level of confidence in his distributor. The distributor must function with a high degree of Quality. The distributor must sell Quality.

The starting point for the Quality distributor must be in the selection of the products he intends to distribute. No matter how well you service what you sell, if you sell anything other than a quality product you cannot, over the long run, be of any real value to your customer. The distributor can and must be selective in the acquisition of product lines. The prospective product manufacturer should be carefully surveyed by the distributor to determine if his house is in order and if he is capable of P.D.Q., the first time and every time. The distributor cannot successfully sell his customer if the distributor himself does not have confidence in the product or its manufacturer.

Another common distributor mistake is taking on every product he can get, just to increase gross sales. Any increase in gross sales under these circumstances will be amazingly short-lived. This "we sell everything" or broad line distribution concept is a real trouble maker. The more products you sell, the less knowledge you can have of each, and with insufficient product knowledge, you do your customer more harm than good. The more products you stock, the more incapable you become of stocking any one product in sufficient depth, for obvious economical reasons, to do your customer a service. When the buyer calls the distributor, he wants to hear four words: It's on the shelf. The narrow line concept of distribution does more to satisfy the needs of the customer, in that the sales force can acquire more product knowledge per line, and the inventory dollar can be better spent simply because there are fewer products to know and stock.

The Quality Distributor must also recognize the need for adequate material and quality control. Just because the manufacturer shipped it and said it was in good shape and as ordered, does not relieve the distributor of his responsibility for assuring compliance with the customer's purchase order. Nothing is easier or faster than a simple visual/mechanical receiving inspection to cover such items as proper quantity, proper configuration, required test data, and shipment damage. If you have a high level of confidence in your manufacturer, you can rely on the tests that he has performed and rest assured that he has test data on file. Once the incoming material is accepted, it must be placed in stock in an orderly fashion and appropriately identified and logged on inventory records. Prior to shipment the material must again be inspected to insure against shipping material that has become defective due to handling or shelf life. In order to assure timely delivery to the customer, the distributor must have a documented procedure for expediting factory orders before they are due. Even if the factory delivery is delayed, the customer will not be angered if he is advised of the delay before the due date.

If a problem of product quality should arise, the responsibility to the customer lies with the distributor, and not specifically with the manufacturer. It is up to the distributor to initiate corrective action, not the customer. The distributor salesman should know his product well enough to be able to speak as a representative of the manufacturer.

The quality distributor salesman must be more than a salesman. He must first be an applications engineer in order to relate his customer's needs and requirements to the products he is representing. If the "Sales Engineer" can satisfy his customer's requirements and help his customer solve his problems, the selling will take care of itself. The distributor, above all, deals in service, and the quality of the service he renders will determine his success or failure.

Here we are, back to that old cliche: Quality doesn't cost—it pays. There is a slow but definite trend toward narrow line quality distribution. For those willing to make the commitment, the rewards are great. For those who are not—our sympathy.

The need is great; the numbers are few. We need Quality Distributors to support and enhance the business and industrial markets of the world.

Chapter 14

QUALITY CONTROL IN THE OFFICE

With all of the millions of offices around the world today, I find each of these to be a major challenge for quality minded management and personnel. I doubt that the surface has been minutely scratched in this vital area which is so conducive to all of the practices and principles of Quality Control, Quality Assurance, Value Analysis, Training, and Motivation. However, management has not recognized the need for Quality Control in the office, nor do they fully understand how Q.C. applies, nor how Q.C. can save many thousands of lost hours and save great amounts of dollars in small, medium, and large offices.

I would briefly like to cover some specific cases to enlighten you with regard to the simplicity and effectiveness of a Quality Program in your office.

First, we must understand that the A.S.Q.C. Standard C-1 applies to any office operation. Please read the Standard again and take it paragraph by paragraph until you have formulated a simple program that is efficient and effective for your office. Yes, you can and will make some changes in the early stages. But, if you evaluate your operation in simple detail, lay out your organization chart in Functional Form, and relate the tasks of the personnel as they relate to the organization, you will be on the road to Quality Control in the office. Just put on paper what actually takes place. Put on paper what your people do or are supposed to do. This is a great opportunity to communicate organizational responsibilities to your people. I know this is old and basic, but it is still very much the case today. How can you expect someone to adequately do their job when you really didn't tell them what you wanted or expected them to do in the first place? I find this to be a great universal management problem. Management assumes too much. They assumed you knew how and when and why and where you and your job got together. And, as always, when we assume too much, we get into trouble. Management forgets to train, indoctrinate, and orient the employee. All too often, it becomes, well, here's your desk or work station—John or Mary will show you what to do. Six months later, the employee has bad habits and probably isn't doing what you expected. Management assumed too much and the employee was a victim of circumstances. This happens every day in offices, shops, and industry all over the world. Take corrective action. Start a total quality training and motivation program today.

You can start with a "Type it Right the First Time Program" or "File it Right the First Time Program." A motivational poster program is just as effective in the office as it is in the manufacturing areas. Quality and safety in the office go hand in hand, just as they do in the production areas. I think it's time that management and personnel recognized this and started working together as a total quality office team.

Let me speak to the President or to the Office Manager for just a moment. In a recent study, it was determined that you lose $2.49 every time a letter goes wrong. You lose even more in prestige and effectiveness when a letter goes out with errors. If you multiply the number of letters, purchase orders, contracts, and miscellaneous paper work times $2.49, I believe you will begin to understand the magnitude of your problems. If you are your secretary's or typist's inspector, (and in most offices, **you are**)—then I believe you can also recognize that you are the highest paid quality inspector in the company!! At this point, you may want to evaluate your personal involvement in the control and assurance of quality in your office and soon after you do this, I believe you will embark on a total and continuing quality assurance program.

What do you need to start? Well, I've discussed that briefly in previous paragraphs, but let me list them for you.

1. Read and understand the chapter on Universal Quality Program Requirements.
2. Plan and formulate a simple quality program which will be efficient and effective for your office. If you can't do this because of circumstances, obtain professional assistance to start the program properly.
   - A. Evaluate your operation in simple detail.
   - B. Describe your firm, products, and services for personnel and customer introduction and orientation.
   - C. Lay out functional organizational chart(s).
   - D. Relate tasks of the personnel in words on the charts.
   - E. Document what actually takes place by job and create job descriptions.
   - F. Establish flow chart of paper work through the office so everyone can see what takes place when, why, where, who, etc.

G. Document the program and procedures.

H. Implement your total program for the control and assurance of quality.

3. Obtain a motivational poster program with typical posters as shown in Chapter 3. The quality motivation portion of the total program is likened to a company's product advertising program. You must keep selling and promoting quality (the product) on a steady and continuing basis for results. Maintain and place the quality posters where the people can see them on a continuing basis. Change the posters on a planned schedule basis for maximum effectiveness.
4. Management must administer and audit the total quality program for cost effective results.

To illustrate some of the above for you, I have included a condensed version of our basic quality program which you can use for a guide.

QUALITY CONTROL IN THE OFFICE
THE CONDENSED
"QUALITY PROGRAM, POLICIES, AND PROCEDURES"
of
C. L. Carter, Jr. and Associates, Inc.
Management and Personnel Consultants
Dallas, Texas

APPROVED: C. L. Carter, Jr.

C. L. Carter, Jr., President

INTRODUCTION AND ORIENTATION

We are management and personnel consultants. We are a cost effective, profit oriented, professional service organization, structured to provide guidance, direction, and technical assistance to those who request our help. Our services are international in scope. As professional consultants, we specialize in quality control, quality assurance, vendor evaluation, cost reduction, training, and motivation. We are both a vendor and the vendee, that is, we buy and we sell. Our services are provided for all types of small, medium, and large business, industry, government, educational organizations, commercial firms, and offices. For example, we can provide services to companies engaged in consumer and industrial products; military hardware; missile and space programs; marine and oceanography oriented equipment; components; systems; distributors; calibration labs; service organizations, and manufacturing operations of any size, which require specific levels of quality and reliability. We provide systems, programs, and procedures for the control and assurance of quality as tailored to the specific needs and requirements of the client.

Our Personnel Search and Placement Services are for management and personnel in the technical, engineering, administrative, managerial, and executive levels. We serve individuals and companies on a confidential professional basis.

Our technical publications, books, film, slides, and other training and motivation materials are marketed internationally to firms and individuals.

Prospective clients are invited to discuss our services in detail as related to their current or long range needs.

Our professional organization as described herein is ready to work with you. Our total impact program is designed to provide you with full-time professional assistance on a part-time basis.

PURPOSE, POLICY, INTENT

The purpose and intent of our total quality program is to assure customer satisfaction in all phases of our business. Our policies and procedures are documented to meet the intent of the American Society for Quality Control C-1 Standard. Professional services and technical assistance are provided at the lowest over-all cost. The integrity of our management and personnel shall be unquestionable and of the highest caliber.

All supplies and services are controlled at all points. Discrepancies are prevented or readily detected. Timely and positive corrective action is taken immediately. Instructions and records are maintained and controlled.

The authority and responsibility of those in charge of specific duties are clearly stated and are outlined in the reference section on detailed Organization Charts.

All work conducted within our office and facilities is controlled completely. It is our intent to do the job right the first time for cost effective control and assurance of quality. A motivational poster program is maintained on a continuing basis.

All work shall be performed in accordance with the documented proposals, contracts, or purchase agreements, as signed by the President.

MANAGEMENT PLANNING AND PROCEDURES

The President requires that all work be performed in an efficient, cost effective manner. Management personnel have the responsibility, authority, and organization freedom to identify and evaluate quality problems and to initiate, recommend, and provide solutions. Management plans and programs are provided by the President and his staff. Our functional management organization charts are shown in the reference section.

All work is presented in clear and completed documented instructions and is typically outlined in the reference section on flow charts.

We maintain sufficient records and data for a successful operation. They are adequate, complete, and reliable. Adverse assignable conditions are promptly detected and corrected. Operations creating losses or excessive costs as the result of defective elements or ineffective operations are identified and changed. We analyze data, trends, and introduce required improvements.

We maintain and use effective quality data to identify the cost of the prevention and correction of non-conforming supplies or services performed by our vendors.

We normally do not manufacture products. However, we are completely aware of manufacturing processes and operating procedures as applicable to business and industry. We are Quality Specialists.

We normally do not design items to be produced. However, as

quality specialists, we provide documented Workmanship Standards for the design and manufacture of the items required. A complete list of our publications is covered on brochures for review and information.

Planning meetings are conducted by the President on a scheduled basis.

PROCUREMENT AND PURCHASING SERVICES

The President or his designated representative assures conformity of all supplies and services procured from our suppliers and/or provided to our clients or customers.

Our Purchase Orders contain a complete description of supplies ordered. We reserve the right to inspect at the source of our suppliers, depending upon the type of supplies purchased.

We provide Vendor Quality Assurance Services for our clients. Professional Vendor Surveys are conducted by our quality personnel. We document all surveys, analyze the results, and provide a full written report to the client. We qualify sources of supply, provide source inspection and expediting assistance for our clients' purchasing and quality organizations.

BASIC OFFICE FUNCTIONS

All basic office and processing operations are done under controlled conditions. Documented work instructions are issued for the operation of the copy machine, stencil machine, electric typewriter, etc. There shall be a maintenance contract on the IBM electric typewriter(s) and any other equipment as designated by the President. The copy machine is serviced and maintained by the manufacturer on a scheduled basis. Specific problems are to be reported direct to the respective company for immediate corrective action.

Inspection and monitoring of any of the above shall be done on a random basis by the President or his designated representative.

The President or his designated representative shall visually inspect all outgoing work, material, and correspondence to consulting clients or customers. Corrective action and re-inspection shall be made as necessary.

Delivery of books, training and motivational aids, etc., to the customer shall be done by mail, special delivery, in person, or as designated by the customer's order. Discounts are allowed for quantity purchases. Our terms are net, ten days. Ordering forms and brochures are available on our services, publications, and training and motivation items.

We maintain and adhere to standard operating procedures for day-to-day functions within our company.

The secretary to the President shall maintain control of our offices. Desk tops and file cabinet tops shall be free from loose correspondence. Such correspondence shall be properly filed for reference. All mail shall be answered promptly. A record shall be maintained of all telephone calls for timely communication, coordination, and control. When the President and/or other management and personnel are out of town or otherwise away from the office, daily communications shall be maintained as a minimum. Complete communication, coordination, and cooperation shall be maintained by all management and personnel at all times.

The stock room shall be orderly in that bookcases, cabinets, shelves, etc., shall provide storage space for brochures, bulletins, and any other supplies and goods. Labels shall properly identify contents.

Customer satisfaction, quality, value, safety, service and integrity shall be the basis for the operation of our business. Our people are responsible for the quality of that which they do.

SOME FINAL THOUGHTS FOR YOUR CONSIDERATION

As you have read our condensed quality program, you can see that it is both an internal and external functional program for our own management and personnel and for our clients and prospective clients.

Your total quality program should be a dual purpose program also. It should be designed as a communication, coordination, and cooperation media for your people and as a sales and marketing tool for use with your customers.

Quality control in the office is the concern of every form of business, industry, or government in the world. Please remember, planning, simplicity, and understanding are the keys to any cost effective quality program. Establish and implement your total quality program now.

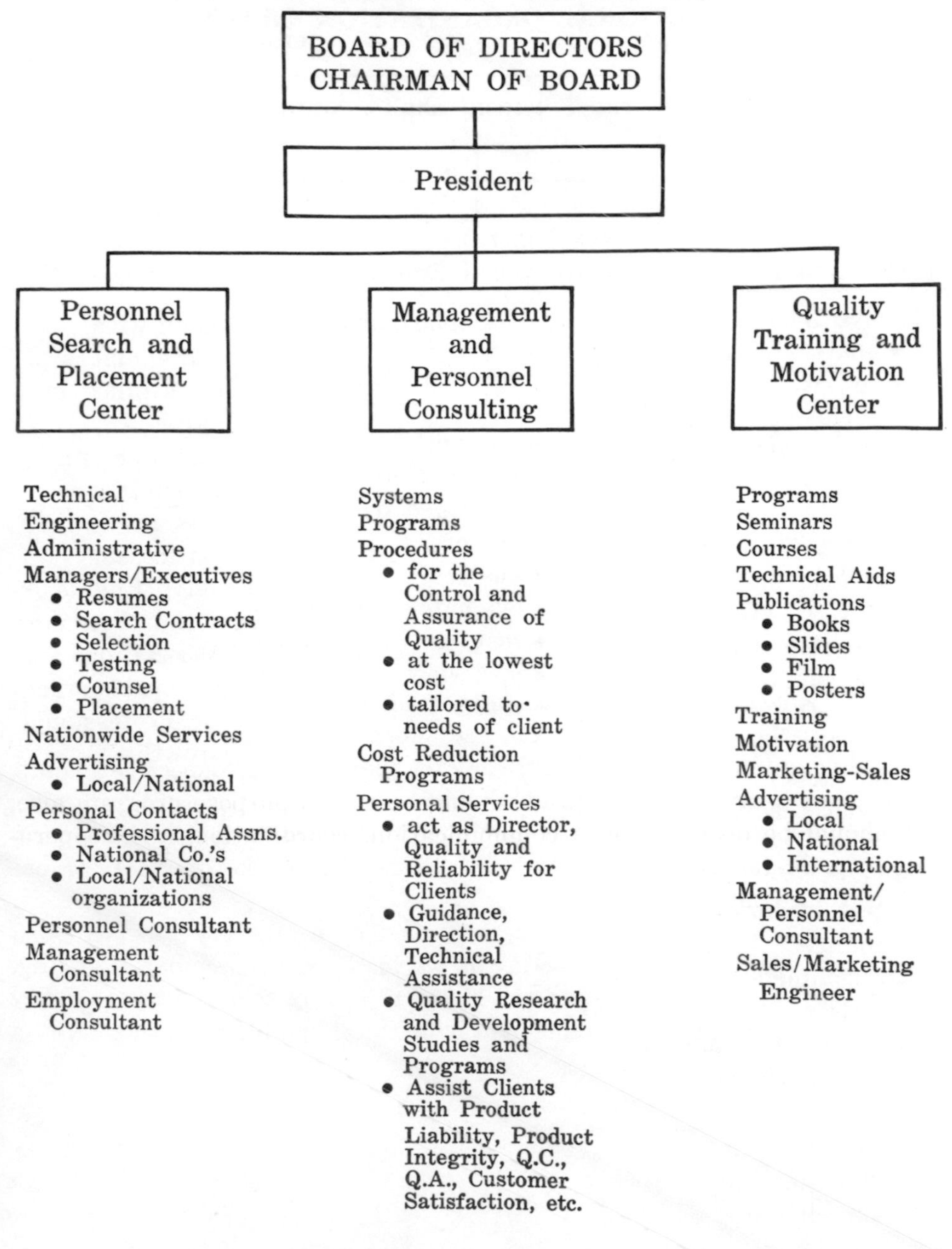
C. L. CARTER, JR. AND ASSOCIATES, INC.
BOARD OF DIRECTORS
CHAIRMAN OF BOARD
President
Personnel Search and Placement Center
Management and Personnel Consulting
Quality Training and Motivation Center
Technical
Engineering
Administrative
Managers/Executives
• Resumes
• Search Contracts
• Selection
• Testing
• Counsel
• Placement
Nationwide Services
Advertising
• Local/National
Personal Contacts
• Professional Assns.
• National Co.'s
• Local/National organizations
Personnel Consultant
Management Consultant
Employment Consultant
Systems
Programs
Procedures
• for the Control and Assurance of Quality
• at the lowest cost
• tailored to needs of client
Cost Reduction Programs
Personal Services
• act as Director, Quality and Reliability for Clients
• Guidance, Direction, Technical Assistance
• Quality Research and Development Studies and Programs
• Assist Clients with Product Liability, Product Integrity, Q.C., Q.A., Customer Satisfaction, etc.
Programs
Seminars
Courses
Technical Aids
Publications
• Books
• Slides
• Film
• Posters
Training
Motivation
Marketing-Sales
Advertising
• Local
• National
• International
Management/ Personnel Consultant
Sales/Marketing Engineer

**PERSONNEL SEARCH AND PLACEMENT CENTER
FUNCTIONAL ORGANIZATION CHART**

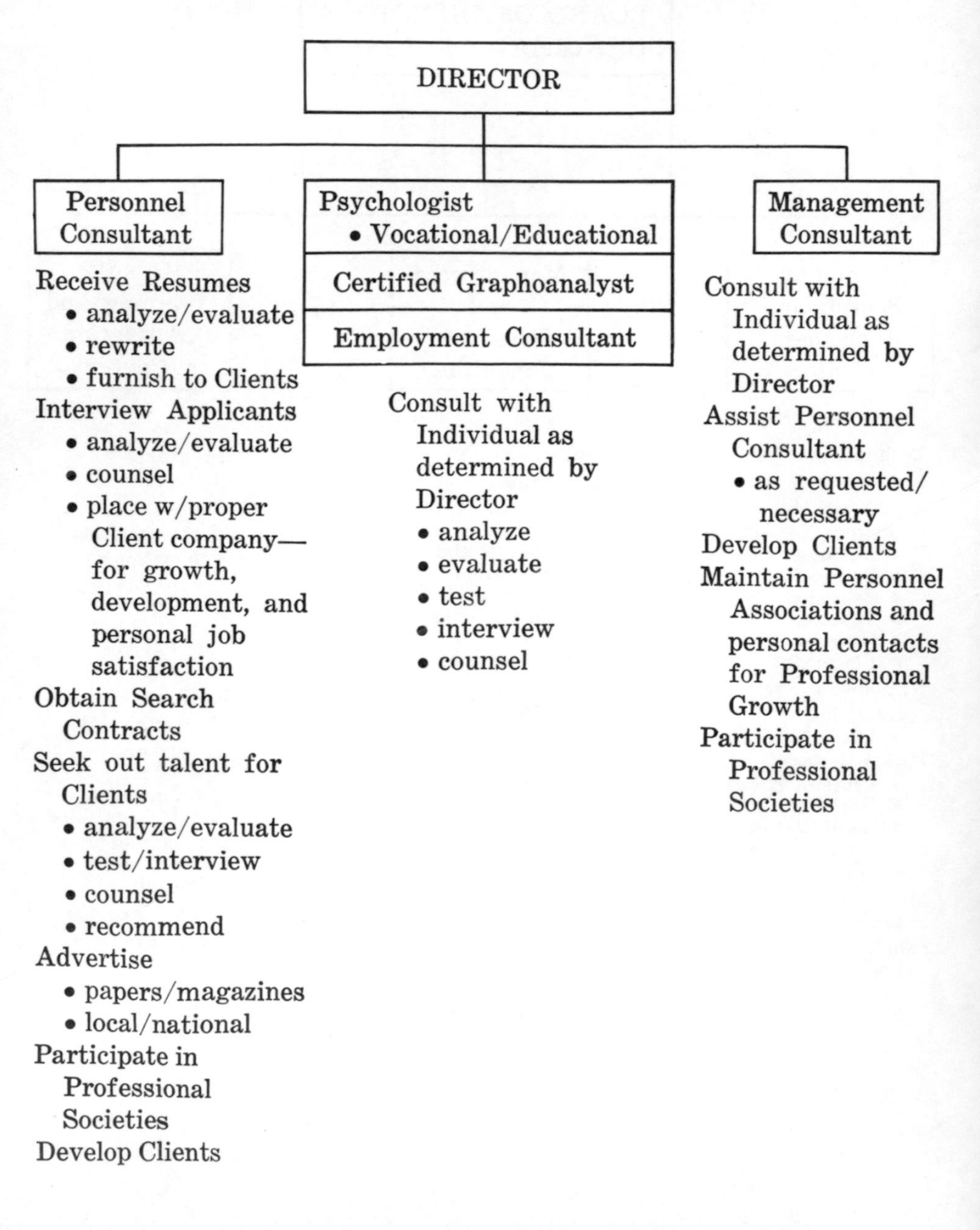

FLOW CHART
PERSONNEL SEARCH AND PLACEMENT CENTER

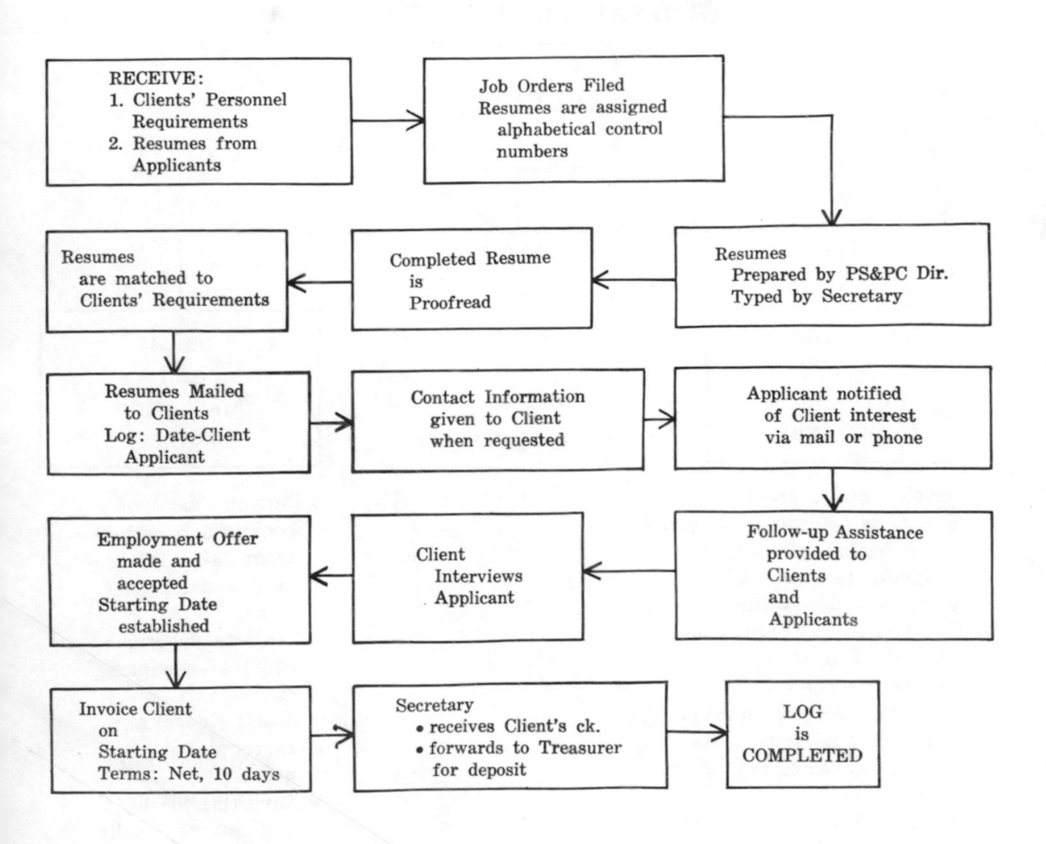

MANAGEMENT & PERSONNEL CONSULTING
AND
QUALITY TRAINING & MOTIVATION CENTER
FUNCTIONAL ORGANIZATION CHART

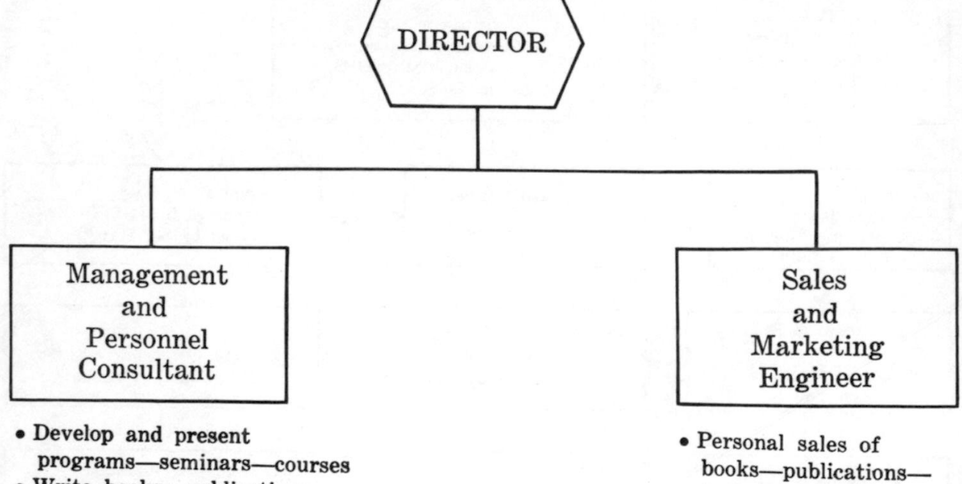

Management and Personnel Consultant

- Develop and present programs—seminars—courses
- Write books—publications originate technical aids, pictures—slides—films
- Write technical papers and present at professional society meetings
- Train and develop management and personnel for clients
- Personal development of individuals
- Consult with clients as needed to solve problems. Develop systems and procedures, etc.
- Assist Sales and Marketing with brochures and literature
- Develop clients
- Provide Guidance, Direction and Technical Assistance
- Quality Assurance Research and Development
- Work with and assist Clients in all phases of Product Liability, Product Integrity, Quality, Customer Satisfaction

Sales and Marketing Engineer

- Personal sales of books—publications—technical aids to local and national firms
- Promote programs—courses—seminars, etc.
- Assist Consultant as requested and necessary
- Advertise locally and internationally
- Develop clients

FLOW CHART
FOR ORDERING PUBLICATIONS
BOOKS, FILM, ETC.

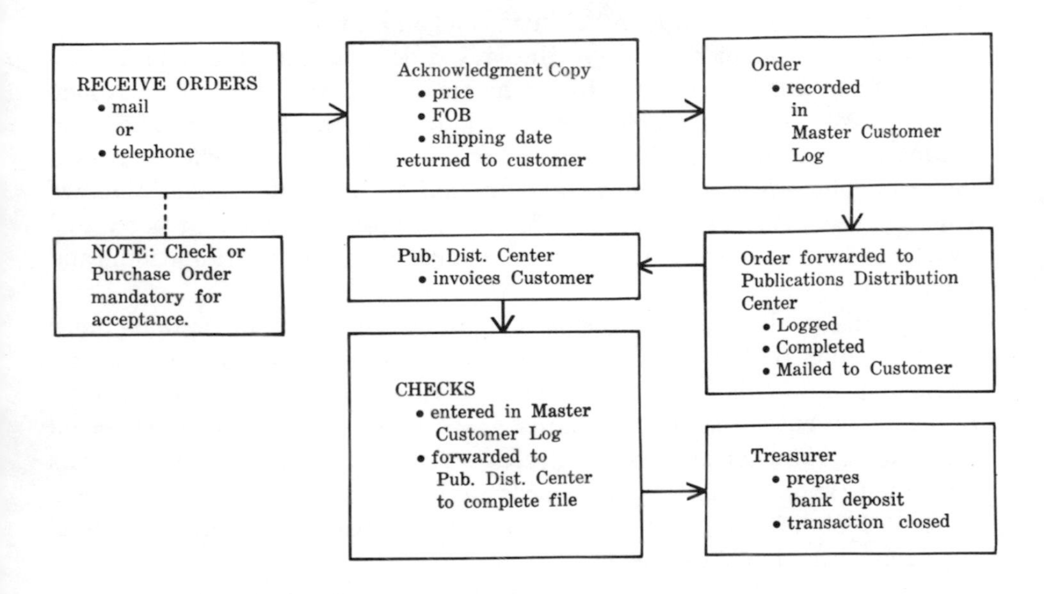

Chapter 15

QUALITY—VALUE—INTEGRITY, "TODAY"

With quality, reliability, value, cost reduction, safety, service, and integrity of products, personnel, and services being in the world spotlight from poor quality, reliability, and maintainability; the heavy emphasis on product reliability; the stated design, manufacturing, quality control, and workmanship problems associated with the Apollo tragedy; Mr. Nadar's much discussed and published work on the vital subjects of the inadequate safety of our automobiles; to the increased government intervention on quality and safety, it would appear that we must concentrate our efforts on the age-old management and personnel problems as caused by inadequate communication, coordination, and cooperation.

In this modern day of the many fabulous computers, management and personnel find themselves unable to communicate in understandable terms on day-to-day problems. The coordination problem of production and inventory control remains as a major bottleneck in most all companies. Internal and external cooperation at all organization levels has given way to lies, deceit, words, and trite phrases to cover up a general lack of integrity on the part of management and personnel on a nation and world-wide basis.

Executives, middle management and functional personnel in small, medium, and large business, industry, educational, and governmental organizations do not understand, nor do they have a basic knowledge of, systems, programs, and procedures for the control and assurance of quality, reliability, value, cost reduction, safety, service, and integrity. It is a vital necessity for all levels of management and associated personnel to understand and be capable of directing the systems, programs, policies, and procedures to achieve factual results for the benefit of their organizations, companies, and for basic customer satisfaction. It's about time "Management and Personnel" stopped giving lip service to the customer. It's about time "Management and Personnel" started to get their "Houses in Order." It's about time "Management and Personnel" began to listen to customers, learn from experience and live up to their sales and marketing words and phrases. Management and Personnel must openly accept the responsibility for whatever they produce or do. It's about time we realized and understood "What's going on."

THE COMMERCIAL AND INDUSTRIAL SCENE

Today, we are plagued with typical phrases such as "Quality Built in, Not Added On"; "Premium Quality Beer"; "Mark of Excellence"; "Space Age Reliability", to name a few. These should be questioned. I would ask the public to challenge some of these words, terms, and phrases along with me. We should ask, "Who established the Standards of Excellence? Who established Premium Quality Standards? Who established the Workmanship Standards for Quality and Reliability?" Answers may be difficult to find.

Automobile Integrity

When average people must take their new cars back to the dealer five, six, and seven or more times, trying to obtain adequate corrective action of quality, reliability, workmanship, and safety items, and still have the same problems, I think you will agree that we are in serious trouble in all areas of quality, reliability, value, costs, safety, service, and particularly in the vital area of integrity.

The typical problem areas mentioned can be found every day in every city, town, business, and industry all over the world. To be quite specific, we can relate the problems to you as a typical individual who purchases a new car, washing machine, dryer, television, repair and maintenance services—to name but a few. How is that "Complex System"—better known as your Car? How many trips have you made to the dealer for service? Were all those trips necessary, or could the dealer have done the job right the first time at a lower cost and retained the customer good will and satisfaction? Did you get the normal run-around lip service treatment, or are you one of the lucky ones who somehow received a good car the first time? When they kept your car for several days, did they give you a courtesy car to drive, or did you have to rent one for $3.00/day? The dealer's "Rent A Car While We Work on Yours" is a new, money-making idea. When you gave the dealer the "List of Problems", I am assuming that you communicated with him in an honest effort to assist the dealer in locating and correcting the "Problems with his Product." Did the dealer coordinate and cooperate by taking positive, corrective action to eliminate the problem or cause? I think I can safely say that we both wish he did—or had—or would ... Let's just say that "Time is Money" and our time is sometimes worth as much—if not a lot more—than the dealer's time. Did you ever stop to realize that the manufacturers and dealers are using the public as inspectors? It's true. You are being used, and at no cost to the manufacturer or dealer! Automobile manufacturers are making the cars more unmaintainable each year. This means that you and I can't work on our cars anymore. One reason is that we would break the warranty, and secondly, we haven't the special tools!!! There are the good guys and the bad guys in all businesses, industries, educational, and governmental organizations. But really, I find it hard to believe that I'm always the one with the only complaint—or have you heard the popular "That's the **first** complaint we've ever had." or, "We have never seen or heard of **that** problem before." or, **"We never** have complaints." ... Some day a complete book on Automobile Dealers, Quality, Value, Service, and Integrity will be written. In the meantime, let me share a few experiences just to ease my mind, and compensate for all the frustrating time we have all invested over the years. Let's explore one or two of mine in detail. I would be interested in discussing your experiences if you have time to write to me.

Over the years, we have purchased several different new and used cars in various sections of the country. It appears however, that most all dealers have the same basic traits when it comes to marketing, sales, service, quality, value, safety, and integrity of products, personnel, and services as rendered for some pretty high costs to you and me. They generally lack Quality, Character, Truth of Marketing and Sales Approaches, The Real Interest and Value of the Customer and his being satisfied, Real Interest in Safety, Real Interest in providing the Best Products and Services at the lowest cost, and most important of all, they apparently lack Integrity. Everything seems to be the "Surface Treatment", or the "Once Over Lightly Treatment." The Individualism or Personal Approach appears to be just about gone. The Indifferent, That's Good Enough, I Don't Care approach appears to be coming on very strong. I firmly believe there are "Accidents Created" by Attitudes of: Indifference; That's Good Enough; I Don't Care; or, We'll Catch That Minor Item the Next Time He Comes Back for Service. I will relate the following as a true and actual case history.

"Mr. Carter, if I could get you $200.00 more for your car right now, would you buy this beautiful automobile tonight? I'm not sure I can, Mr. Carter, but if you will sign this 'Agreement to Purchase' at this price, I'll sure take it in and try to get the General Sales Manager to accept it. Will you do that, Mr. Carter?"

I must say at this point, that I have been through so many of these frustrating situations that my heart goes out in deep sympathy to those who are in the process of buying a car. I also had reason to believe that the salesman would not be successful in getting his General Sales Manager to accept "The Deal", as they commonly call it, and so I signed the Agreement. As in a Stage Play: Enter the General Sales Manager and exit the Salesman, who has "done all he could"—shakes your hand and leaves. You are now in the hands of "The Closer." The General Sales Manager now states that instead of your getting $200.00 more, he can't possibly trade with you for that figure because of Dealer's cost of the car, make-ready costs, service costs and other various and sundry reasons why it's really going to cost you $150.00 **more** than the salesman quoted. At this point, you wish it were possible to sue for breach of promise; call the Police, based on Robbery; or, after you have been to several dealers—you begin to wonder why there aren't more laws enacted to protect the public from this type of **marketeering.**

Did someone say Integrity? Character?

Let's not forget what else the salesman and assistant sales manager (or was he the Vice President?) said about the warranty and guarantee. We have been told recently that it wouldn't cost you one penny for repairs, parts or labor for the entire period, and that all you had to do was put gas and oil in that beautiful automobile for two years or five years, etc., etc., etc. Are we really to believe this?

Well, let's continue. As it happened, I was introduced to the President of a dealership, and we negotiated what turned out to be a "House Deal", which in effect means that you by-passed the salesman. As it turned out, the car had to be special ordered, because at "That Price" they just couldn't get one from another dealer, and besides, this car had the big engine (at the suggestion of the President—for my driving satisfaction). Five weeks later, I called about my car—I hadn't heard anything from the dealer. They would check. I was advised it would be in on Wednesday. They called on Saturday to tell me my car had just come off the truck, and would not be made-ready until Monday. I took this opportunity to review the "Raw New Car" direct from the factory, which is only about 15 miles away. I was quite depressed with my findings. I had ordered a convertible with a white top—the top was tan. I had ordered the Mirror Group, which included a remote controlled mirror and the day-night mirror—the car had neither. I had ordered a "Safety Flasher"—it was not there. The car had deep scratches on the hood, doors, trunk and other areas. I had, in effect, conducted a

"Minor Type Receiving Inspection" on this car, which was to be mine. This was also a personal, pre-screening of the Dealer's make-ready operation. I was, in effect, conducting a personal study.

I received a call from the assistant sales manager to come for the car. We went down as a family to accept the car, and were very unhappy with our "Made-Ready—Personally Approved New Car." I looked through the rear window and saw the rear of the seat, the raw bare car, top motor, etc. They had not assembled the rear deck cover. The car still had major portions of the factory protective coating on the exterior, which indicated it was probably given a quick wash job. All of the original scratches were still intact, plus several more. In brief, we, as a family, "Rejected and Refused to Accept the Car." The assistant sales manager said he was sorry. The President said he was sorry and indicated that there was a lack of integrity on the part of the individual who signed off and released the car, and also on the part of the assistant sales manager, because he had not checked the car either. The President indicated he had "People Problems". I indicated that he had a lot more problems than he realized, which included his Product, Planning, Procedures, Over All Program, Personnel, and a lot of dissatisfied customers.

We left the car for another "Make Ready" attempt by the dealer with all sorts of verbal assurances that it would be Ready and Right this time.

I won't belabor this case, because it could continue into a full length book (a true novel) covering the trials and tribulations connected with this car . . . including the dealer trying to raise the price on the last day. I reluctantly accepted the car on July 2, in order that we might have it on our wedding anniversary and use it over the long weekend. The car has been back to the dealer over and over again for the same troubles—at one point they kept the car for 2½ weeks. When I left the dealership, the car had a loose ball joint, and had to go back again! I have strongly recommended that they take the car back and that we start over again with a new one. Nothing has worked, and I seriously question the validity of "The Mark of Excellence".

I have studied, explored, and been the victim of Automotive Marketeering. On several of my speaking engagements, I have discussed "Typical Cases", and it is interesting to note the facial expressions and understanding smiles concerning the individual reactions of the people—because if the truth were known, I would believe that 95% of you have experienced these same ridiculous and frustrating case histories. I recall one man who said he had been trying to get his windshield wipers fixed for 5 months. Another man bought one of those Excellent Cars and the windshield wiper only hit part of the window. The dealer was not able to get a replacement from the factory for weeks —they hadn't thought about taking a wiper from another new car. Did someone say Safety!! Some cases are a little humorous ... a family bought a new station wagon; drove it half way home (about 2 miles), and the engine stopped. The gas gauge said half full—but the tank was empty! This happened 2 or 3 times, and on one occasion, they were towed in for 30 miles ... same gas gauge problem. The same station wagon was to have had a "Roof Top Carrier", but it was not available. The wife was called by the dealer to have the carrier installed. She had an appointment, but was promised immediate attention by the dealer. She took the wagon down and went shopping at a nearby shopping center, while the carrier was installed. She returned and found the car right where she had parked it—no carrier. Did someone say Integrity? Did someone say Customer Satisfaction?

I recently saw a billboard automobile ad which read, "We're Volume Minded". How true that is—Throw it together and get it out ... Ship it!! That's good enough—Let it go—We're Volume Minded—Fleet Prices to all Customers ... about all I can say is, "It reads well in the newspapers and sounds good on radio and television, but please don't believe all of their words, phrases and promises." Perhaps someday a sign will say, "We're quality minded." Perhaps someday there will be a money back guarantee on automobiles.

In 1950, we bought a new "Club Coupe". Today it's known as a "Fast Back". When it rained, we had more water inside the car than there was outside. The "Rear Wing Window" didn't fit the body cutout and the upholstery rotted out from being wet. Water came in from under the car, and it came in the trunk from the top and bottom. That was many years ago when a car was hard to get. There were paint runs, scratches, leaks, bolts and nuts missing, sloppy and careless workmanship, poor quality and reliability, better maintainability, but more maintenance required, and a host of other pro's and con's concerning the car, the dealer and you, the owner and driver.

Today, we still have the same problems as they relate to you and me, the car, and the dealer. However, today there are different terms, words, phrases and gimmicks used. The salesman talks about the projected 2-year-old resale value of a car you haven't purchased yet. He can't truthfully predict that $500.00 more in resale anymore than he can your getting 20 miles per gallon on regular gas in city driving. They talk about transferring the warranty and about other incidental sales and marketing items, but I find one thing is more common as I visit from dealer to dealer, and that is "They don't really know their own products, either technically or from the practical viewpoint."

When you ask a salesman the horsepower of the car, or tire size, or wheelbase, or whatever your question might be, I find them looking on the side of the car, looking at the tires, or looking at the specification sheet. This doesn't do a whole lot for my confidence level in the dealer, and the conversation is only 5 minutes old. And so we come back to some basic fundamentals of Quality Assurance Theory, Principals and Applications.

A. It pays to know your dealer or supplier.

B. The dealer should know that "Up Front Quality, Value and Integrity" starts with Trained, Qualified Personnel at all levels of the organization, and that "Up Front Quality, Value and Integrity" will lead to lower costs, higher profits, and satisfied customers who return to the dealer they have confidence in.

C. It takes a lot of Sound Management Planning, Action and Dedication.

D. It takes Good Design Engineering and extensive Quality and Reliability qualification and life tests to assure the product will function as stated under all conditions for the stipulated period of time.

E. It takes a Good Quality Assurance Team—a planned program and motivated personnel.

There isn't any magic formula. It just takes Quality, Value and Integrity of Management, Personnel, Products and Services.

Insist On and Receive Quality

Are we receiving a Quality Automobile for our money? Since there are no formal Quality Specifications, I would have to say no. I say this, because "You're buying what they're selling." You are not receiving the Quality of Product that you should because you're receiving only that which you insist on in the way of Quality, Workmanship, Reliability, Function, Value and Service. If you will accept a car with screws missing, a slight dent in the front fender, scratches in the paint, misfitting parts and moulding, doors that do not close properly, plus hundreds of other things too numerous to mention, then that's what you're going to get—for the same amount of money. If you let them get away with Poor Quality, Poor Workmanship, etc., then you are making more money for them, because they have to do less for the same money. I think it's time we applied some "Common Sense Quality Assurance" **before** we buy and pay for that so-called Excellent Car. Be your own best inspector. Insist that it be right before—not after. If you wait until "after" you have purchased and started to pay, then it will always be an uphill fight to obtain corrective action. Insist on having it right as it should be, and the way you want it—before you pay. Why not make the dealer "Do It Right The First Time", and let him make the investment in Customer Satisfaction before and after the sale. I would suggest that the dealer and the factory get a lot closer together, because the dealer really isn't getting a quality product to start with. Have you seen the newspapers play up "Auto makers calling back cars and trucks for possible dangerous defects."

Protection for the Public

I would entertain that some serious thought and study be given to enacting some protective legal recourse for the Public in the form of withholding full payment until full satisfaction is received. I think we should invoke a "Satisfaction Guaranteed or Your Money Back" clause in Automobile Purchasing Contracts. I think we should insist on and be able to obtain Automobile Integrity without having to go to court.

Have Women Sell Automobiles

To the best of my knowledge, there are very few saleswomen in the Automobile Business. Since the Automotive Industry appears to be building cars with wall-to-wall carpets, interiors suited to the female eye and taste, it would be a refreshing, invigorating and stimulating concept of developing integrity into the Automobile Business by having women sell "whole cars" with less options. Perhaps the ladies can insist on obtaining and providing Quality, Value, Safety, Service, and Integrity. It's worth a try! Particularly with the equal employment opportunity act.

HOME APPLIANCE INTEGRITY

Women today are the first to complain when the toaster fails to function; or, their iron doesn't work; or, the dryer timer doesn't work; or, the washer won't stop spinning; or, the roast burned, because the timer didn't go off; or, several hundred other major items of interest to those who are living and working with modern home appliances.

I have, on many occasions, explained the brief story about "Planned Obsolescence", or "Planned Reliability Wearout", or "Planned Replacement for Planned Business". Many people are not aware of these terms, and are rather amazed when they realize what's going on. My wife called and said the steam iron was broken and did not get as hot as it should. She wanted me to look at it, fix it, or get it fixed. I looked, examined, and analyzed. It was not made to be maintained. I couldn't get it apart, so how could I fix it? It would have cost us about one-third the cost of a new steam iron to possibly have it repaired. I asked some simple questions. How old was the steam iron? Three years old. How much did it cost? $12.00. At $4.00 per year, and used most every day, I decided the steam iron was probably made to last three or four years and then be replaced. It didn't pay to repair the iron, so we bought a new one.

One woman said, "They just don't make things like they used to." Well, I guess not. They used to cost more and had less working parts and features. Now you have steam irons with spray features, gauges, and other added extras—at the same or lower costs. With this in mind, they also plan them to wear out for Built-In Replacement Business. This is a new way of life and a new way of doing and developing business for many, many people all over the world. As mentioned before, it takes a lot of Engineering and Management Planning, extensive Quality and Reliability qualification testing to assure the product will function as stated for the stipulated period of time.

Quality, Value and Integrity in the Commercial Consumer market is where you separate the Men from the Boys in most every aspect of business. I am a firm believer in the old phrase, "Quality Doesn't Cost —It Pays." If we look at one or two case histories, I think you will begin to understand.

A remodeling job was underway, and the new electric oven was installed in the kitchen. When the current was applied the whole electrical system in the oven was destroyed and certainly could have caused a major fire in the home. The failure was caused by improper wiring within the oven—the oven was wired wrong at the factory. The oven was removed and replaced. Costly? Yes, indeed.

A new refrigerator was delivered and connected. The housewife attempted to open the refrigerator door while turning the water faucet off. The refrigerator was "Hot" because of a wiring error, and when she touched the faucet (ground), she was shocked and thrown across the room to the floor. A serious or fatal accident could have occurred. She was not seriously hurt. The refrigerator was replaced. Costly? Yes, indeed.

A portable bed vibrator was purchased recently. It was delivered and connected. It vibrated for a while, and then began to get very noisy, and finally stopped operating. It was replaced. The second vibrator was cracked on receipt and returned. The third vibrator was somewhat noisy, which instead of being relaxing, actually kept you awake. The fourth vibrator is currently still operating. Costly? Aggravating? Yes, indeed.

A color television was delivered and connected. This was for a "Free Trial Period—Over the Week End." The color was most beautiful in every respect on Friday evening and Saturday. Saturday evening the set started to snap, crackle and pop. It popped once too much and stopped operating. When they installed the color television, they scratched the new furniture. The color set is gone, the scratches remain. Costly? Aggravating? Yes, indeed.

These are but a few, and I'm sure you could name many, many more personal case histories.

MOTIVATING CUSTOMERS

I find that some companies care. Some companies talk a good game. Some companies are careless, and some companies could care "less", and thereby, just don't care about you, me, or anyone. As long as you keep buying inferior quality, and do not insist on Quality, Value and Integrity—the "I don't care company" will continue to produce and sell it to you. But one of these days, when the competition tightens, and you begin to insist on Quality—the "I don't care company" will fall by the side of the road and be forgotten.

I would be pleased if you would remember this phrase: "The Problem doesn't know the name of the Company." It's realistic, true, and applies to all companies everywhere.

It's always a pleasure doing business with a Personalized Company that cares about you, me, their products, and their services. Because they care, they insist on—and have—Quality, Value, and Integrity.

I think it's about time to start management on the task of motivating customers with 'Quality, Value, and Integrity.'

PRODUCT LIABILITY

There are law suits in the Courts based on product liability, product and safety negligence, workmanship defects, and many other items. We will be hearing more and more of product and safety liability, particularly in the automobile, food and drug, appliance, and airline industries. The auto makers are calling back cars and trucks for possible dangerous defects. This is a new law, requiring auto makers to report to the government possible or known dangerous defects which could be safety or related accident problems. These could be steering, brakes, ball joints, tires, welding, plus many, many others. Perhaps you have heard the phrase, "Accidents are caused and created; they don't just happen." Well, there is a lot of truth to those words. When the car is demolished and the driver is dead, how do you establish that the brakes failed or the steering failed? At this time, we do not have an official Federal Automobile Authority to reconstruct demolished automobiles as we do in the Federal Aviation Authority. Perhaps we will have, in the near future, when all the automotive data is gathered and analyzed. I would suggest that the automotive industry establish their own Automotive Accident Authority before the federal or state governments invoke a mandatory accident authority. The automotive, consumer, and airline industries should be capable of controlling and assuring the quality, value, safety, service, and integrity of their products and services. If they do not, the government will certainly try. I am sure the F.A.A. and/or the Civil Aeronautics Board investigates why planes crash and why aircraft doors 'open' in flight and people are extracted in flight through the open door.

These items as mentioned are the cause of product liability and airline liability law suits. Industrial and Business Management must recognize and react to their responsibility for Product Liability, Quality, Value, Safety, Service and Product Integrity. All Commercial, Industrial and Government related suppliers are involved. Management should have Professional Legal Advice, Professional Insurance Advice and Professional Quality Advice.

PRODUCT QUALITY COMPLAINTS GROW

Corporate purchasing agents and buyers are complaining louder these days about the poor quality of manufactured products in all segments of business and industry. There are several conditions blamed. Some of these are:

1. High volume production—get the product out—ship it.
2. Cost cutting to take pressure off profit squeeze.
3. Pressure on vendor for lower cost material creates skimpy quality.
4. Deterioration in workmanship due to tight labor market in which marginal employees are used.
5. Loss of pride in workmanship by skilled workers.
6. Products not completely tested based on complexity.
7. Poor design—lax service.
8. Push vendor for delivery—product not right when you get it.
9. Poor production planning and material control.
10. Vendor management attitude.

To discuss each of the above individually would be repetitious and time consuming, since I believe they have all been covered throughout this book. I mention them here because these are common complaints of purchasing management and because all ten appear to be tied-in someway to product liability.

Purchasing and quality managers should work closely to procure quality products on time at the lowest total cost. The vendor must have a total quality assurance management team and program in order to produce quality products, on time, at the lowest total cost.

Chapter 16

THE QUALITY TEAM

The Quality Team is a group of people working together to provide a quality product or service, on time, at the lowest cost, for a profit. It does not matter what business or industry you are associated with, management, marketing, engineering, manufacturing, and quality must work together as a team to achieve an acceptable end product and to build the integrity of the company. Whether the organization is large or small has no bearing on the teamwork necessary to achieve these goals. In order to discuss the total quality team, we have chosen the analogy between a professional football team and the business and industrial organization. To do this, we must associate football personnel to those of the business and industrial organization.

The association is as follows:

Head Coach	— Management
Recruiting	— Personnel
Buyers	— Purchasing
Scout	— Marketing
Asst. Coaches	— Engineering
Players	— Production
Spotters	— Quality Control
and	and
Referees	Quality Assurance

HEAD COACH versus MANAGEMENT

A Head Coach sets the type of offense, defense, and the spirit of the team. Management has the same goals to achieve, by setting the philosophies of the company and the motivation of the personnel. Just as a football team has to have pep talks, the company personnel have to be motivated to produce a quality product.

To achieve the goals of management or the Head Coach, there must be a workable system. There are various publications available to pursue the many types of management systems.

The Head Coach has offense plays, such as ground and passing plays. For defense, he can choose a zone, a blitz, a man-to-man, or any combination.

Management has quality control handbooks and government specifications available such as:

Quality Assurance, Quality Control and Inspection Handbook by C. L. Carter, Jr.

The Control and Assurance of Quality by C. L. Carter, Jr.

Quality Control for Management by Paul Peach
Total Quality Control by A. V. Feigenbaum
Quality Control Handbook by J. M. Juran

MIL-Q-9858	—Quality Program Requirements
MIL-I-45208	—Inspection Systems Requirements
MIL-C-45662	—Calibration Systems Requirements
NPC 200-3	—Inspection System Provisions for Suppliers of Space Materials
ASQC STD C-1	—General Requirements for a Quality Program

The system must be simple, brief, direct, and functional. The Head Coach and management must develop the system, then train and motivate their personnel.

RECRUITING versus PERSONNEL

Although the scout does some advance screening for potential talent, the recruiting, selling the team to the person, the interviewing and final offer must come from personnel, industrial relations, and/or direct from management. Both functions are vital to the Quality Team for without them there would be no players, no product, no team.

BUYERS versus PURCHASING

Buying the uniforms, equipment and all of the many associated items that it takes to run a good ball team requires talented buyers. The purchasing organization is the heart of the Industrial Quality Team in that they must buy products and services on time, at the lowest total cost, with acceptable quality and reliability consistent with the end item being produced. The purchasing-quality relationship must be based on mutual understanding and total teamwork to achieve total quality. You wouldn't have a quality team without a professional purchasing organization.

SCOUT versus MARKETING

The scout is very similar to marketing. A scout searches out personnel and recommends them to the coaching staff for review. Whereas, marketing has to beat the bushes with a product which has to be a saleable item. In the day and age where the emphasis is placed on "quality of a product," marketing has to present the quality and reliability of the product. This is where marketing must depend on engineering, manufacturing, and quality control to work as a team to build quality and reliability into the product. Just like the scout, when he recommends a player, he relays all the attributes of this particular player to the coaching staff. Marketing has the same responsibility of obtaining all the specifications and having them reviewed by engineering, manufacturing, and quality. A little planning in advance will alleviate problems downstream.

Field problems are something else. Complaints should be handled through Marketing and/or Quality. Make sure they are coordinated with Engineering and/or Manufacturing. The most efficient means of keeping customer relations is a fast turnaround on the correction of any complaint.

ASSISTANT COACHES versus ENGINEERING

The Assistant Coaches review and study the various plays for their respective assignments. Engineering has the responsibility of designing quality, reliability, and maintainability into a product.

Just as the assistant coaches teach and assist the players in the development of the new plays, engineering plays a vital role during the 3 P's, which are:

First, **Prototype**—is the period when a product or item is being evaluated and qualified to determine standards.

Second, **Pre-production**—is the coordinating period between Quality and Manufacturing.

Third, **Production**—is the period when everything is supposed to run smoothly as long as the engineering changes are kept at a moderately low level.

The Assistant Coaches tell the players, that if the play is executed in a given sequence, there should be no doubt that a touchdown will occur. Engineering should try to remember the popular Quality Trademark, "DO IT RIGHT THE FIRST TIME." Engineering change orders are costly.

PLAYERS versus MANUFACTURING

Manufacturing and the players of a football team have a similar job to perform.

Although a player may have played football in elementary school, high school, and college, this does not mean he can play professional football. The progress he made through the lower schools taught him the fundamentals of football. But, he still has to go through a training program months before the season begins, and continue each week in preparation for the upcoming games. Manufacturing has the same principles to follow. Before a new product is put into production, there must be a training program for the key personnel. Also, during this period, the assembly techniques, processes, and testing problems can be researched and solved before production goes into full swing. One of the most important projects to remember is, having trained and qualified operators before releasing them to the Production Department. Train and Qualify them before, not after, they foul up production.

There is one thing that a football team does, which also is helpful and related to Manufacturing, and that is—having a back-up player when one or more is out of action. To manufacturing and purchasing, this means having more than one supplier so that schedules are met, with no downtime for Production. This also means having key personnel in reserve, all through the manufacturing operation. Flexibility is the key word.

SPOTTER versus QUALITY CONTROL AND QUALITY ASSURANCE

To really get this particular topic across, we need to set the scene for a football game. Sunday afternoon, and the crowd is anxiously waiting for the game to start between the Dallas Cowboys and the Green Bay Packers. The coaches are giving their respective players a last-minute "pep" talk. The spotters for the two teams are sitting in the press box with the telephone or head-sets pressed against their ears. The spotters' role begins with the kickoff, and their role is very important to the coaches and players. The spotters will relay messages to coaches and/or players as to why defense or offense plays are not working. Also, he will make suggestions as to what might help particular plays. Quality control and quality assurance, like the spotters, are the arms and legs for management, marketing, engineering, and manufacturing. They send reports to management, make sure marketing has a saleable product, and provide liaison between engineering and manufacturing. The other important quality objective is standardization of workmanship and documented procedures for your organization.

The quality team is not limited to management, marketing, engineering, manufacturing, quality control, or quality assurance. Each one must work individually and collectively as a group. Each organization must have "total" teamwork to meet the demands of today's customer.

Let me leave one thought with you—"When has one man on a football team been outstanding without the help of his fellow teammates?" You can be an asset to your organization by effective Communication, Coordination, and Teamwork. You are a vital part of the quality team.

Chapter 17

COMPETITION

Competition is the Key to the free enterprise system. Almost any person can go into business and perhaps be a competitor to your business. This happens every day. On the other hand, there are businesses that close and go out of business every day. Competition based on Quality, Value, and Integrity is Good. Competition based on Quality, Value, and Integrity is Healthy. Competition promotes, motivates, and stimulates Businessmen, Industrialists, Bankers, and all of the Management, Personnel, and consumers involved in the business world. Competition creates new Ideas, new products and services, new markets, and new business which benefits everyone concerned, including you and me.

I have heard so many business people say, "Our Business is very competitive, our profit margin is very low, our markets are getting smaller, our business is bad, our business is cutthroat ..." We have all heard the claims of individual businesses and industries in terms of, "We control the market" or "We have a noncompetitive item." We have also heard of "price fixing" and other means and methods of trying to "control or close a market." Some of these cases have involved "Name Brands" and one or more of the corporate executives have or are serving jail sentences. Someone had to make the corporate sacrifice, and I feel reasonably sure the executives involved will be remunerated by the corporation for their "Sacrifice." Why mention this? Competition, market control, and power will do strange things to the Small, Medium, and even the Giants of Industry. Politics is the same, if not worse. Government contracts and Consumer-related items are also involved in "Management Games." But, regardless of the circumstances or the language used in playing "Management Games," we must always return to Quality, Value, Integrity, and Fair-play based on clean and honest competition.

Friendly competition can be highlighted by my professional association as Past-President of the Employment Board of Dallas. This professional organization with a firm code of ethics and business practices is made up of Private Employment Agency owners. We meet once each month for friendship, fellowship, exchange of ideas, and to discuss mutual areas of concern to the membership. We are all "Friendly Competitors" and I can honestly state that I have never seen a more cooperative and friendly group of dedicated, professional personnel placement specialists.

QUALITY-VALUE AND PRODUCT INTEGRITY FROM JAPAN:

About 10 years ago, the Japanese were known for making Inferior Quality and had the name of Junk Merchants. This was a very serious problem which the Japanese Government and Industry recognized. Quality, Value, and Integrity of Products was going to ruin them as an industrial nation unless they jointly acted to correct their vast Quality problems. They collectively established a Quality Program Plan to control and assure the Quality, Value, and Integrity of Products made in Japan and exported to the world markets. The Japanese established a Goal and a Quality Program Plan to assure themselves that Japan would be Number 1 in the Quality Market places of the world. Let me repeat: They dedicated themselves to being Number 1 in the Quality Market places of the world. They are achieving their goal on a slow and steady pace.

Japan is or will be your major Industrial Quality Competitor.

The Japanese Quality Program Plan is merely putting into practice the Theory and Application of Quality Control and Quality Assurance. We do a lot of Quality Preaching, provide a lot of Lip Service to Quality but do not practice what we preach. This could be our downfall unless we get with it and start "Doing" instead of "Talking."

The Japanese Quality Program was enacted into Law which was agreed to by Industry and the Government. In simple terms, the Law requires each firm to have a system for the control and assurance of Quality. It further required the establishment of "Specialized Trade Institutes" which would provide Quality Assurance Inspections and Audits to Assure Product Quality prior to any product being shipped from Japan. These "Quality Assurance Institutes" were established and have been in operation for several years. I have personally seen their "Acceptance Stamps" on Products Exported from Japan. The Quality Assurance Institutes assure the manufacturer, the Government, and the customer that Products shipped from Japan meet or exceed the Quality Standards for Performance, Value, and Workmanship. Products which do not meet the Standards are rejected and not permitted to be exported from Japan.

This has been a very cost effective system for the Japanese, and they have not deviated from their original Quality Assurance Plan. They have only tried to strengthen the Plan, the Program, and Improve the Quality of their Products. This Quality Assurance Program has allowed the Japanese to command the Respect of Professional Photographers for producing the finest cameras and optical equipment. As I see it, they plan to command the Respect for Producing the finest Quality, at the lowest overall cost, product by product and industry by industry. They are now making some very fine Inspection and Test Equipment, and I would be safe in predicting that unless we Recognize and do something about the "Quality Competition Challenge"; you will be buying Quality Assurance Inspection and Test Equipment from the Japanese because it will be the Best Quality at the lowest cost. Some of you are already using Japanese Equipment to check the Quality, Accuracy, and Reliability of your products.

There have been reports on the excellent quality of Japanese Steel. The Quality and Workmanship of the Japanese Automobiles are reported to be outstanding. The Tape Recorder, Radio, and Television Industry is aware of the Japanese Electronics Sales and Performance records. I have recently read an article concerning "No Incoming Inspection Required" based on the Japanese Export Quality Assurance Program.

Several of our U. S. companies are opening manufacturing firms in Japan to achieve Maximum Quality at the Lowest overall cost. I feel sure the Japanese Export Quality Assurance Program is a Key contributing factor in favor of attracting Industry to Japan.

Mr. Chairman of the Board, Mr. President, Mr. Vice President of Manufacturing; Mr. Vice President of Quality and Reliability—This is your competition. Do you accept the challenge, or are you going to watch them pass you by?

As a Professional Quality Engineer, as a Professional Management and Personnel Consultant, I accept the challenge to maintain the Respect of business, industry, and the consumers of the local, national, and international market places of the world. You must have the ability to achieve quality, value, and integrity of products, personnel, and services. Are you ready to meet the challenge? Are you ready for competition in Quality, Value, and Integrity? Set your goals, establish your Policy, develop your Quality Program Plan and then follow the Plan. Dedicate yourself to "Achieve Superior Quality Control." Dedicate yourself to A.S.Q.C.

Chapter 18

WHAT MANAGEMENT NEEDS TO KNOW

I won't go into a long dissertation on what management needs to know, except to say that they need to know that they MUST have and provide Quality, Value, and Integrity, and without these, they will fall and probably fail.

Here are some things for management to know and remember:

1. Professional Quality talent is a must. To try to 'get by' with anything less, is refusing to face reality, which will result in spending twice as much money in an effort to correct, compensate, and re-establish customer confidence.
2. Management must have a documented and functioning system for total control and assurance of quality and it doesn't matter who the company is, the service it provides, or the product it manufactures. The Quality system will save money and bring in new customers.
3. Do not fight the Quality System, which has been professionally established and tailored to the needs of the organization. The Quality System will work only if management wants it to work. You must invest before you earn dividends. Quality pays dividends.
4. Quality Control and Quality Assurance are not 'hocus-pocus', costly, necessary evils. Please refer to the definitions in Chapter 2 and learn to understand what Q.C. and Q.A. can do for you. If you think Q.C. and Q.A. are trying to do something to you, I would suggest that you have amateurs working for you, who need to be replaced with professional quality people. Remember, Q.C. and Q.A. will do cost-effective things for you. They will make you money.
5. You need a total quality team and not a partial quality effort.
6. You need to listen to professional quality people and make them a vital part of your executive management team for quality, value, integrity, reduced costs, and increased profits at all levels of the organization. Remember, you are liable for defective products and sub-standard or poor workmanship.
7. You need to train and motivate your management and personnel at all levels on a planned, consistent basis.
8. You must have documented Quality Workmanship Standards. Your people must know what to do and how to do the job right

the first time. Remember, if you do the job right the first time, you are doing the job at the lowest cost. The second time around, rework, and ultimate scrap, will always cost you money and reduces profits substantially.

9. Do what you agreed to do. Make it like the drawing and deliver the quality product on time.
10. The average percentage of quality personnel to total plant personnel varies from 6% to 12%. This will always be governed by your type of business, type of product, and qualifications of management and personnel. Use these figures as a guide, and remember, Professional Quality people will always strive to reduce inspection with the ultimate goal being to eliminate inspection by having qualified production people doing their jobs right the first time. In this way, you can go to the quality audit and random sample basis for quality assurance.
11. Your quality people should always be providing you with quality records in the commonly understood language of dollars and cents. You should be able to relate these figures to sales, cost of materials, vendor quality, in-process quality costs, scrap, rework, and any other items in the budget.
12. You are responsible for the control and assurance of quality. If I were you, I would have professional talent in all key positions; buy from good, qualified quality vendors; have good machines, processes, procedures, and people making a good quality product, right the first time, for satisfied customers, at a good profit. Remember, Management is Responsible for the Control and Assurance of Quality. With Product Liability coming on so strong, if I were you, I sure would get very much interested in the Control and Assurance of Quality, because it can save and make more money for you.

Chapter 19

QUALITY CONTROL AND QUALITY ASSURANCE BENEFITS

Practical and Statistical methods of quality control, quality assurance and reliability as developed and practiced by some of the nation's leading industries, educational organizations and governmental agencies have provided outstanding benefits in the following typical areas:

1. Advanced up-front planning and systems analysis
2. Improved quality of purchased items
3. Improved manufacturing process controls
4. Reduced scrap, rework and downtime
5. Reduced costs and decreased rejections
6. Improved quality and reliability of products and services
7. Savings in labor and material
8. Improved vendor-vendee and customer relations
9. Improved production, production control and materials management
10. Improved accounting, budget and clerical functions
11. Forecasting for sales, marketing and management
12. Research, design and development
13. Produceability and maintainability
14. Computerization functions for data storage and retrieval
15. Corrective action, when and as needed
16. Decision making tools for management
17. Reporting trends, problems and reactions
18. Maintaining control, standardization and assurance of quality, value, safety, workmanship and integrity

These modern methods and techniques tell us when and where to look for sources of trouble. We are thereby warned when problems are imminent and have helpful reports to assist us in averting the trouble. We are advised when it is economical to change processes, programs, procedures and people. We can save time and money by the effective use of the combined scientific and practical phases of quality control and quality assurance methods and techniques which are being used in and are recommended for typical business and industry such as: Aircraft (commercial and military); Automotive; Candy; Chemicals; Clothing; Communications; Computers; Distributors; Drugs; Dishes; Electrical